Concrete constituents
and mix proportions

11.004 First published 1974

SBN 7210 0905 0

Price: £5.00

Designed by Edward Fittall
Published by the Cement and Concrete Association
52 Grosvenor Gardens, London SW1W 0AQ

Computer composition/print in England by
Eyre & Spottiswoode Ltd at Grosvenor Press

Concrete constituents and mix proportions

B. W. Shacklock, MSc, FICE, MIStructE, FIHE
Director of Administrative Services
Cement and Concrete Association

Cement and Concrete Association

BARRY W. SHACKLOCK graduated from the University of Durham in 1948. He then joined the Royal Air Force and was commissioned in the Airfield Construction Branch, where he was involved with the construction of various new airfield works. On leaving the service he joined the Research and Development Division of the Cement and Concrete Association. There he undertook a number of research investigations including the design of high-strength mixes, gap-graded concrete, the relation of aggregate specific surface to concrete workability, plastic and drying shrinkage, elasticity, air entrainment and the frost resistance of kerbs. The most extensive of his investigations was into the use of concrete in flooring.

In 1958 he joined the Association's Advisory Service and concentrated initially on roads and civil engineering works. He made detailed studies into the practical application of admixtures in concrete and the use of ready mixed concrete, and has written a number of articles and papers on these and other topics. In 1967 he was appointed Deputy Director of the Advisory Division and assumed responsibility for a wide range of the Association's advisory work, acting as technical adviser on several films dealing with concrete practice. Since 1971 he has been Director of Administrative Services for the Association but still maintains his interest in many aspects of concrete technology.

Mr Shacklock has been a member of several BSI committees concerned with concrete, and is one of the authors of the Handbook on the Unified Code for structural concrete, CP 110 : 1972, which forms the basis of much of the practice recommended in this book.

CONTENTS

Concrete mixes have for many years been examined by research workers with the object of relating the nature and proportions of the constituent materials — cement, aggregate, water and possibly admixtures — to the properties of the concrete. Very considerable amounts of data have been amassed, and periodically the data have been correlated, in a manner that enables the concrete producer to assess the constituent materials available to him and to determine the most suitable proportions to meet the requirements of the particular construction work to be undertaken. Further, over the years, changes occur in the methods of manufacturing materials and the techniques for producing, handling and placing concrete, and a re-examination of the methods of selecting or using particular constituents and of the methods of proportioning those materials becomes necessary. This, together with the ever-widening range of concrete properties requiring examination, has prompted the writing of this book.

The scope of the book is therefore rather wider than is generally understood by the term 'mix design', which can be defined as the determination of the most suitable proportions of the constituents of concrete taking into account the properties of those constituents and the workability, strength, durability and finished appearance required of the concrete. Whilst this form of mix design is undoubtedly valid, and will continue to be so as new constituents are developed by research, the very large quantities of concrete which currently must be produced as economically as possible mean that the emphasis tends increasingly to change from one of selecting suitable constituent materials for a good mix design to one of making use of those materials available within a reasonable distance of the construction site. A considerable emphasis is therefore placed on the examination of constituent materials with a view to making the best possible use of them.

The various stages involved in producing concrete which are discussed in this book can therefore be summarized as:

(1) an appreciation of the current methods of specifying concrete;
(2) an examination of the properties of the constituent materials of concrete;
(3) the estimation of suitable mix proportions to meet specification requirements, using, where possible, recorded data of the concrete produced previously at the particular plant or site;
(4) the making of trial mixes in a laboratory to justify the mix proportions selected, where little or no previous data exist regarding the selected mix;
(5) the making of trial mixes under site conditions; and
(6) adjustments to mix proportions during production to meet day-to-day variations in the constituent materials

and to ensure continued compliance of the concrete with the specification requirements.

Concrete structures can be designed to a number of different codes of practice and it is impossible to include all the minor provisos associated with each one; the appropriate code should therefore be examined in relation to particular projects. Nevertheless the most recent Code of Practice, CP 110, 'The structural use of concrete', is by far the most up-to-date, and it is therefore from this code that some of the data in this book have been obtained — for example, the concept of characteristic strength and the data on the durability of concrete in Tables 5.2 and 5.3.

Note on units
The book is written using metric SI units. Imperial equivalents have been included in parentheses for convenience, except where it has been past practice to use metric units. However, the accuracy to which imperial equivalents are given varies depending upon the significance of the number; for example, when reference is made to a compressive strength of 35 N/mm^2 the equivalent would correctly be quoted as 5050 lbf/in^2, but where the technical point being discussed does not justify such accuracy the equivalent is shown as 5000 lbf/in^2. Similarly, in a discussion of aggregate sizes, the imperial equivalent to 10 mm is 3/8 in. but, in a reference to cover to reinforcement, the corresponding imperial value is, by custom, ½ in. The weight of a bag of cement is taken as 50 kg.

CHAPTER 1

A background to mix design

1.1 Some thoughts on mix design

The object of mix design is to determine the most appropriate proportions in which to use the constituent materials to meet the needs of construction work. In particular the concrete should
(1) comply with the specification requirement for structural strength which is usually stated in terms of the compressive strength of standard test specimens;
(2) have satisfactory durability in the environment in which the structure is placed;
(3) have a satisfactory appearance in those situations where it is exposed to view;
(4) be capable of being mixed, transported, placed and compacted efficiently; and
(5) be as economical as possible.
Clearly any successful mix design must be preceded by a sound and reasonably detailed knowledge of the constituent materials — the cement, aggregate, water and possibly admixtures — not only because this leads to a better understanding of the process of mix design, but because a more efficient result will be obtained; for example, the use of an aggregate local to the construction work would generally result in the most economical concrete, but where the concrete is required to have an unusually high strength this may not be so and a rather more expensive aggregate from further away might enable a concrete of higher workability to be used and thus save significantly on placing costs.

The process of mix design has often been broken down into three stages as follows:
(a) an estimation of the correct mix proportions based upon either published data or past experience and upon a knowledge of the properties of the aggregate to be used, which may involve some preliminary testing;
(b) small-scale trial mixes, usually in a laboratory, using the aggregate in a condition of known moisture content;
(c) full-scale trials on site before the actual construction starts.
From this simple breakdown, which applied reasonably well in the 1950s, two contrary trends have emerged and are worth consideration. The large majority of structural concrete used in the United Kingdom nowadays is produced in either ready mixed concrete depots or precast concrete factories. In these instances a continuity of work is maintained and the experience gained while producing concrete for one contract automatically provides data for use with the next. Therefore, in (a) above, the emphasis is naturally placed upon past experience rather than published data, and (b) becomes completely unnecessary once a depot or factory has become established. The contrary trend is shown by the ever-increasing range of new materials developed; for example, lightweight aggregates and admixtures. In this instance the emphasis has often to be placed on published data since little past experience may exist, and small-scale trial mixes are probably essential. Further, in this latter trend, the data needed for mix design cannot be standardized because the new materials themselves often have widely differing properties. Both these trends do, however, add up in one respect: the 'standardized' mix design procedures, such as those published in Road Research Road Note 4[1], 'Design of concrete mixes', are no longer as important as they used to be.

Much mix design work has been undertaken since the publication of the first edition of Road Note 4. Some of this work has been based upon a consideration of aggregate grading and particle packing. Theories and equations, some very complex, have been derived in attempts to represent good concrete properties; none to date has become widely accepted, partly because complex theories require so many supporting data — for example, a knowledge of the specific surface characteristics of the aggregates — that they are not economically justified. Further, no mix design procedure developed to date is sufficiently accurate as to be usable either without previous data regarding the strength properties of the particular sources of cement and aggregate or without benefit of trial mixes, which involves waiting for the results of strength tests.

For these reasons, the mix design procedures favoured in this book are those in which data, obtained from a wide range of mixes, are collated in such a way as to enable an estimate to be made of the required mix proportions in as simple a manner as possible, generally using only those parameters — type of cement, type and grading of aggregate, workability, strength and durability requirements — as can be used or known on the construction site. The more sophisticated parameters, such as aggregate voids ratio or aggregate specific surface, are avoided, though a knowledge of them is often helpful in particular aspects of mix design; for example, the relation between aggregate specific surface and water requirement[2, 3, 4] is the basis of the recommendations for combining aggregate gradings in Chapter 7.2, and a knowledge of the aggregate voids ratio[5] assists with the design of exposed aggregate concretes in Chapter 6.3 and of concrete for pumping in Chapter 6.23.

1.2 Variations in concrete properties

Basic to the understanding of concrete mix design is an appreciation that all properties of concrete vary during production from day to day, from batch to batch and even within any batch. In order to allow for these variations and yet still to meet the requirements of job specifications, various factors of safety are built into a mix design; these factors of safety will generally result in the concrete containing a rather greater quantity of cement – generally the most expensive ingredient – than would be needed if all the variations could be eliminated. However, the elimination of all variation, if it were possible – and it is not – would increase the cost of the constituent materials and of the concrete production. In practice the most economic concrete is made by balancing these factors; close control is maintained over the production of the cement and a rather lesser, though generally adequate, control is maintained over the aggregate supplies to satisfy the requirements of the vast majority of work; thereafter reasonably close control over the production of concrete is justified for most structural work and, where the nature of the work justifies it, a much closer control over production is possible.

The extent to which concrete varies is generally assessed by measuring the strength of the hardened concrete in a standardized manner and by analysing the test results statistically. Whilst it is possible to study statistics in considerable depth,[6] this is generally unnecessary for most concrete producers and the following simplified approach is all that is needed for an initial mix design. Statistics can also be of benefit when assessing the results of tests carried out during concrete production; these are discussed in Chapter 7.

In practice the strengths of test cubes, taken at random from batches of nominally similar concrete and plotted as a histogram*, will be found to be of the form shown in Figure 1.1. The curve drawn is the normal or Gaussian distribution curve, calculated from the results shown in the histogram; if a very large number of results were available the shape of the histogram would generally approach that of the normal distribution.

If the normal distribution curves from different construction sites are compared, it will be found that the widths of the curves vary to an extent dependent upon the different degrees of control exercised on the work. The width of the distribution curve is therefore important and is assessed as a

'standard deviation' which can be calculated from the formula

$$\sqrt{\frac{\Sigma\,(x-\bar{x})^2}{N-1}}$$

where N = the number of results
$\bar{x}$ = the average of the results
x = the individual result

Where the standard deviation has to be re-calculated as more test results become available, an alternative equation may be more convenient:

$$\sqrt{\frac{\Sigma(x^2)-(\Sigma x)^2/N}{N-1}}$$

The curve of Figure 1.1 also shows that a small number of test results must be expected to have very low values; this is attributable to the inevitable risk that something will go seriously wrong such as the accidental omission of the cement in a batch. Thus there is no such thing as an absolute 'minimum' strength and modern specifications for strength often state that not more than a particular proportion of test results should fall below the specified value. The average strength needed to meet any specification of this type must exceed the specified value by a constant k times the standard deviation, where the value of k can be taken from Figure 1.2. In practice the proportion expected below the specified strength varies but, in the most recently published documents, it is accepted as 5% in accordance with an international agreement drawn up by the Comité Européen du Béton and the Fédération Internationale de la Précontrainte;[7] the strength specified according to this definition is known as the 'characteristic' strength. In Figure 1.2 the value of k corresponding to 5% of test results being below the specified characteristic strength is shown as 1.64; it is most important, however, to note that the value 1.64 represents an average of 5% of results falling below the specified value and, since specifications for concrete are taken to mean that *not more than* 5% of results should fall below the specified strength, a rather greater value of k should be used for mix design purposes. When, however, it later becomes necessary to examine test results to see whether or not the concrete produced did meet a specified characteristic strength, then it would be appropriate to use the value 1.64, so for the sake of avoiding confusion a value of 1.64 is used throughout this book in accordance with CP 110.

1.3 A breakdown of the factors affecting variation in strength test results

The variability of the results shown in Figure 1.1 can be due to many factors, the more important of which can be listed as follows:
(1) cement strength development properties
    cement from a single works
    cement from several works
(2) water requirement of aggregate
    grading
    particle shape
    surface texture

*A histogram is a diagram in which the number of times a particular result occurs – for example, in Figure 1.1, the number of compressive strength tests results between 33.75 and 35.75 N/mm² – is shown on a vertical scale against compressive strength which is shown on the horizontal scale. The horizontal scale is divided into a number of equal intervals, often 12 to 15, covering the range of results under consideration, and all results within each interval contribute to the number of results shown on the vertical scale.

2

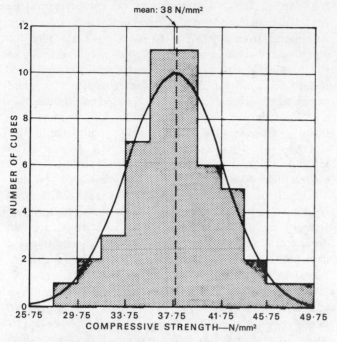

Figure 1.1 : Example of histogram.
(If imperial units were used different but convenient ranges of strength would be appropriate – perhaps ranges of 250 lbf/in².)

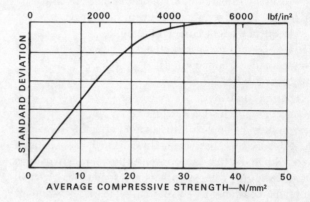

Figure 1.3 : Relation between standard deviation and average compressive strength for any particular degree of control.
The maximum value on the vertical scale would generally be in the range 4 to 8 N/mm² (600 to 1200 lbf/in²); see Table 1.2.

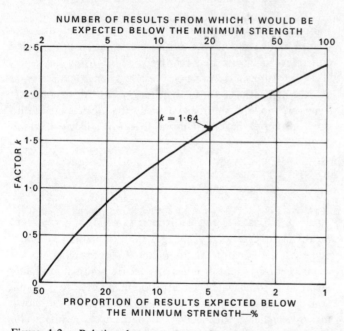

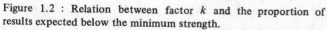

Figure 1.2 : Relation between factor k and the proportion of results expected below the minimum strength.

(3) quantity of cement batched
>   accuracy of batching equipment
>
>   accuracy of batching to indicated batch weight

(4) quantity of aggregate batched
>   accuracy of batching equipment
>
>   accuracy of batching to indicated batch weight

(5) quantity of water batched
>   method of assessing water requirement
>
>   method and frequency of measuring aggregate moisture content
>
>   method and frequency of measuring concrete workability
>
>   accuracy of batching equipment
>
>   accuracy of batching to indicated batch quantity

(6) errors associated with measurement of strength
>   frequency and accuracy of sampling
>
>   weather at time of sampling
>
>   accuracy of cube moulds
>
>   casting cubes
>
>   curing conditions
>
>   accuracy of testing machine

The magnitude of some of the factors affecting the variability of concrete has been investigated by research workers. Some factors are conveniently represented by a standard deviation whereas others are sometimes given in terms of the coefficient of variation, which is the standard deviation divided by the average strength and is expressed as a percentage. For convenience the standard deviation is used for all factors in the following discussion. This is generally correct for concretes having an average strength over about 35 N/mm^2 (about 5000 lbf/in^2) whereas, below this strength, it is generally preferable to use the coefficient of variation. The relation between standard deviation and average strength for any particular degree of control is shown in Figure 1.3.

One of the most extensive investigations was undertaken by Erntroy,[8] some of whose results are summarized in Table 1.1, which shows several interesting points. If the specified strength is to be exceeded by twice the standard deviation, then the average strength required will generally be 1 N/mm^2 (150 lbf/in^2) higher when cement is batched by volume than when it is batched by the bag or by weight. The required average will also be 1 N/mm^2 (150 lbf/in^2) higher when aggregate is batched by volume than when it is batched by weight; further, the required average strength will generally be 0.75 N/mm^2 (100 lbf/in^2) higher when cement is taken from several works rather than from one works. On the other hand, Erntroy observed that a very considerable scatter of results was obtained within any nominal standard of control and that this was probably attributable to varying degrees of care in maintenance of equipment and general supervision; because of this, differences in the required average strength might well be 3 or 4 N/mm^2 (450 or 600 lbf/in^2), as indicated in Table 1.2. Typically, 20% of the 300 jobs examined had standard deviations more than one-third greater or one-third less than the average values found. More recent work on this subject has been reported by Metcalf;[9] the magnitude of variations observed tended to be a little less than those reported by Erntroy.

A further factor which should be considered is the confidence that can be placed upon any standard deviation determined from a set of test results. Even assuming the sampling and testing procedure is correct, the reliability of the standard deviation is dependent upon the number of results on which it is based; for example, a standard deviation of 5 N/mm^2 (700 lbf/in^2) based on 40 results has a 95% certainty of being correct within ±1.1 N/mm^2 (160 lbf/in^2), whereas one based on 100 results has a 95% certainty of being correct within ±0.7 N/mm^2 (100 lbf/in^2). Standard deviations should not therefore be based on less than 40 results, and any value based on less than 100 results should be treated with some reserve. This point becomes significant when the margin between specified strength and the intended target mean strength for mix design purposes is discussed in Chapter 4.2. The standard deviation likely to be achieved in practice from a series of test results will therefore depend upon many factors and it is not possible to predict the result with any great degree of confidence. The values given in Table 1.2 are a guide to likely standard deviation, though it would not be appropriate to undertake an initial mix design based on these figures where the specification for the concrete lays down some other value.

1.4 Variation in the properties of fresh concrete

Fresh concrete can vary in its properties in much the same way as hardened concrete. While the variation in hardened concrete can be assessed relatively easily, using the generally accepted criterion of compressive strength, there is no equivalently straightforward criterion for fresh concrete; however, modern methods of analysing fresh concrete do show promise. Several factors therefore justify examination.

1.4.1 Aggregate properties

Most variations in aggregate properties will to a large extent be offset in practice by changes in the quantity of water added to the concrete at the mixer. Thus, for example, the use of a consignment of unusually coarse sand will probably result in a lower water/cement ratio being used to maintain constant workability, and this may subsequently be shown up by higher compressive strength test results. This concrete may, however, prove harsh and more difficult to handle, leading possibly to honeycombing. It is therefore generally advisable to use slightly higher proportions of fine aggregate than may be found strictly necessary from some other points of view. Nevertheless there are some circumstances, for example when concrete is pumped, where variations in the aggregate properties can be important; particular care must then be taken to ensure reasonable uniformity of supplies. Variation in the particle shape of coarse aggregates can have some effect on the cohesiveness and handling properties of concrete, but the extent of the variation is unlikely to be of significance except in the case of excessively large proportions of shell in marine aggregate.

TABLE 1.1
Breakdown of standard deviation for compressive strength for different standards of control, according to Erntroy.[8]

Item of control	Standard deviation for mean strengths of 35 N/mm² (5000 lbf/in²) or more − N/mm² (lbf/in²)			
			All items	
	Item alone	Item plus testing	Cement (one works)	Cement (many works)
cement from one works	3.05 (440)	3.65 (530)	−	−
cement from many works	3.6 (520)	4.15 (600)	−	−
batching −				
cement in bulk, servo-operated weighing	2.55 (370)	3.3 (480)	4.5 (650)	4.85 (700)
cement and aggregates weighed	3.8 (550)	4.3 (620)	5.25 (760)	5.6 (810)
cement weighed, aggregates by volume	4.55 (660)	4.95 (720)	5.8 (840)	6.15 (890)
cement and aggregates by volume	5.2 (750)	5.5 (800)	6.35 (920)	6.65 (960)
cement and aggregates by volume in a continuous mixer	3.05 (440)	3.65 (530)	4.75 (690)	5.1 (740)
testing	2.05 (300)	−	−	−

TABLE 1.2
Values of standard deviation for different standards of quality control, according to Erntroy.[8]

Batching		Supervision	Standard deviation for average strengths over about 35 N/mm² (5000 lbf/in²) − N/mm² (lbf/in²)
Cement	Aggregate		
weight (servo-operation)	weight (servo-operation)	good *	3.1 (450)
		normal	4.7 (680)
		poor +	6.3 (910)
weight	weight	good *	3.65 (530)
		normal	5.45 (790)
		poor +	7.25 (1050)
weight	volume	good*	4.0 (580)
		normal	6.0 (870)
		poor +	8.0 (1160)
volume	volume	good *	4.35 (630)
		normal	6.5 (940)
		poor +	8.6 (1250)

* About 10% of sites were better than the values quoted.
+ About 10% of sites were worse than the values quoted.

1.4.2 Workability

The workability of concrete is discussed in some detail in Chapter 4.3. For the moment it is only necessary to note that workability varies from one batch of concrete to the next, depending largely on the care with which the batching and mixing are undertaken. The variations should be recognized and allowed for in both the specification and the design of concrete mixes. Although closer tolerances than the following can be obtained they cannot generally be assumed. Slump test results will often vary by ±25 mm (1 in.) or ± one-third of the required value, whichever is the greater. Compacting factor test results will often vary by ±0.03 of the required value where this is 0.9 or more, by ±0.04 of the required value where this is between 0.8 and 0.9, and by ±0.05 of the required value where this is less than 0.8. Relatively few Vebe consistometer test results are available, but it seems likely that the results can be expected to vary by about ±3 degrees or ± one-fifth of the required value, whichever is the greater. If the workability required for a particular purpose is known to have to exceed a certain value — for example, a slump of not less than 25 mm (1 in.) for pumping through a pipeline — the above likely variations should be taken into account in the mix design and a higher average value should be used.

1.4.3 Air content

The air content of air-entrained concrete is liable to vary by up to about ±1.5% from the required value. The average air content from any four consecutive test values should therefore not vary by more than about ±0.75% from the required value.

1.5 Accuracy of mix design

The preceding discussion shows that mix design is far from an exact science and that extreme precision is not justified. The principal objective of a person undertaking practical work involving the design of concrete mixes must therefore be firstly to have a thorough understanding of the constituent materials being used, secondly to have an ability to assess the mix proportions needed to meet the job specifications, and thirdly to ensure there is a reasonable certainty that all the other specification requirements will be met. The accuracy with which the mix proportions should be assessed is not easy to establish, but for the vast majority of work it is probably sufficient that the cement content and the proportion of fine to total aggregate should each be known to within ±5%. Whilst greater accuracy might seem to be preferable and possible, there is a strong probability that unavoidable variations in the constituent materials (both between the initial tests and the full-scale work and during the work) would nullify any efforts at greater accuracy.

1.6 Definition of water/cement ratio

Even the most elementary knowledge of the properties of concrete involves the ratio by weight of water to cement, or water/cement ratio. The lower the water/cement ratio, the better are many properties of the hardened concrete; next to the over-riding requirement that all concrete should be fully compacted if its greatest strength and durability are to be achieved, this water/cement ratio 'law' is fundamental to the making of good concrete. The water/cement ratio is, however, difficult to define because the aggregates in the concrete absorb water inside the particles, often to an unknown extent. There is therefore a choice of either neglecting all the water inside the particles and including just the weight of water on the surface of the aggregate particles plus the water added during mixing (this is then called the 'free' water/cement ratio), or including all the water inside and outside the aggregate particles plus the added water (this is called the 'total' water/cement ratio). It does not matter greatly to the satisfactory making of concrete whether the free or total water/cement ratio is used, provided the corresponding 'free' or 'total' moisture content of the aggregate is used subsequently in the control of concrete quality during production. The free water/cement ratio has the advantage that the ratio has a direct bearing on the properties of the cement paste in the concrete and therefore represents such factors as durability more accurately than a total water/cement ratio; the dis-advantage, however, is that it is less easy to measure the amount of water on the surface of the aggregate particles without disturbing the absorbed water and, besides, the method of measurement involves getting the aggregate into a saturated but surface-dry condition. Conversely, the total water/cement ratio is a less accurate measure of the quality of the cement paste but is easier to measure as it is possible to dry the aggregate thoroughly when measuring its moisture content. However, even this is not very precise because 'total' water/cement ratio, as used in laboratories with air-dry aggregate, is generally taken as including only that amount of water added to the air-dry aggregate. Although the extent of drying in an unspecified air-drying condition can be very variable, it is probably sufficiently accurate to assume that air-dry dense aggregates contain half the total water absorption determined in accordance with BS 812, 'Methods for sampling and testing of mineral aggregates, sands and fillers'.

Some mix design data are expressed in free water/cement ratios and some in total water/cement ratios. It has not been possible to limit or correct all the data in the book to one definition or the other, so both have unfortunately had to be used. The abbreviated term 'water/cement ratio' means free water/cement ratio as is generally understood in practice, and the term 'total water/cement ratio' has been used where this is intended.

CHAPTER 2

Specification of concrete

2.1 Performance specifications

In practice concrete is specified in many different ways, some of which are logical and effective and some illogical, leading to unnecessary confusion and redundant requirements which can in the extreme be irreconcilable.

One of the first essentials should be a clear understanding of whether
(1) the concrete is being specified by its performance (sometimes called an end-product specification), in which case the means by which the end is obtained are not relevant to the specification itself (though they would be of concern to those controlling the work); or
(2) the concrete is being prescribed in detail and, provided the work is carried out to specification, the actual performance or end-product properties of the concrete are no more than the unstated responsibility of the specifying authority.

Neither of these ideals of specification can in fact be achieved entirely. For example, a performance specification may have to include a certain level of resistance to sulphate attack and so have to specify the use of a sulphate-resisting Portland cement, which becomes a prescription. Similarly, a prescription specification might well call for the aggregate to comply with BS 882, which contains the performance requirements that the aggregate shall not contain deleterious materials in such a form or in sufficient quantity to affect adversely the strength at any age or the durability of the concrete. Nevertheless, the gross errors of specifying constituent materials, mix proportions and water/cement ratio as well as strength, or of specifying constituent materials, mix proportions, water/cement ratio and workability, should be avoided as they are likely to prove irreconcilable.

At the current stage of technology, a performance specification should be used whenever possible and should be specified in accordance with the relevant Code of Practice. In general, performance specifications should for preference include the following data:
(1) a description of the required minimum strength of concrete, possibly as a characteristic strength or a grade description* — some recommended values taken

---

*A grade description is merely the characteristic strength in N/mm^2 but without units. The term 'grade' has been avoided in this book because the number ceases to have significance when imperial units are used.

from CP 110, together with limitations on use, are given in Table 2.1;
(2) the type of cement to be used, quoting, where possible, the relevant British Standard Specification;
(3) the nominal maximum size of aggregate;
(4) the type of aggregate to be used, quoting, where possible, the relevant British Standard Specification;
(5) the minimum cement content to meet durability, appearance and other requirements;
(6) the rate of, and responsibility for, testing the concrete and the type of tests to be carried out.

TABLE 2.1
Some recommended characteristic strengths (determined at 24 hours for concrete with high alumina cement, and at 28 days for concrete with any other cement).

Characteristic compressive strength – N/mm^2 (lbf/in^2)	Lowest strength for:
7 (1000)	plain concrete
10 (1450)	
15 (2200)	reinforced concrete with lightweight aggregate
20 (2900)	reinforced concrete with dense aggregate
25 (3600)	
30 (4350)	concrete with post-tensioned tendons
40 (5800)	concrete with pre-tensioned tendons
50 (7250)	reinforced concrete with high alumina cement
60 (8700)	prestressed concrete with high alumina cement

To these six items others (given below) may be added, though it should be noted that none are generally necessary, and none should be used unless the particular circumstances of the work warrant it:
(7) the type and sizes of aggregate to be used, possibly quoting the exact source from which the aggregate should be obtained (this form of requirement might be relevant, for example, when a particular colour or texture is required for some exposed-aggregate concrete);
(8) whether an admixture shall or shall not be used and, if one is to be used, the type and conditions of use (this could apply, for example, to concrete roads where an air-entraining admixture might be essential or to pre-tensioned prestressed concrete where calcium chloride must not be used); in the absence of any requirement, the concrete supplier would be given freedom, subject

to the specificer's agreement, to decide wheth or not an admixture is used.

(9) the maximum cement content to limit the development of heat in mass concrete structures; care would have to be exercised not to make this limit so close to (5) above as to inhibit good mix design;

(10) the workability of the concrete − this would apply where a contractor is specifying concrete to a ready mixed concrete supplier but would be most unlikely to apply to an engineer or architect specifying concrete to a contractor, since details of plant and placing techniques would not generally be known;

(11) the minimum or maximum density of the concrete − the most likely application would be to specify a maximum density for lightweight concrete; particular care would have to be taken to specify the appropriate definition of density (fresh, air-dry or oven-dry) and the appropriate method of test;

(12) the minimum or maximum temperature of the fresh concrete − the most likely application would be to specify a minimum temperature at which work may continue in cold weather.

Concrete mixes should be designed to meet the specified performance requirements. Details are given in Chapter 4 (strength and workability), Chapter 5 (durability) and Chapter 6 (special requirements).

The alternative of specifying concrete by a detailed prescription of the constituent materials and mix proportions has already been mentioned. Certain mixes have been prescribed in various documents under the headings of 'standard', 'prescribed' or 'rationalized' mixes, and several of these are reproduced in this book for convenience. In general, the data specified relate to the quality of the constituent materials, the proportions of the solid ingredients and the workability of the concrete to meet a particular minimum concrete strength.

Several points relating to prescribed mixes should be noted.

(1) The details given must be such that there is a strong probability that the strength, durability and other required properties can be obtained using any of the cements and aggregates likely to be available. Thus any prescribed mix must be related to the particular geographical area from which data were collected to arrive at the particular prescription given. The data in this book refer to conditions in the United Kingdom, though there is no reason why prescribed mixes should not be produced specifically for a more limited area.

(2) The mix details given must also relate to the poorer-quality constituent materials in the area to ensure that the required concrete properties are generally met. In those parts of the area where constituent materials are of better than average quality, the mix proportions prescribed must appear to contain an unnecessarily high proportion of cement and therefore to be unnecessarily expensive.

(3) Prescribed mixes by their nature are likely to be used on small works and at the beginning of large works, where the standard of quality control is not necessarily good or has not been ascertained; therefore the margin (see Chapter 4.2) between the specified minimum strength and the target mean strength used in arriving at the prescribed proportions must be relatively large; this again leads to the use of a relatively high cement content. From these considerations it is clear that a prescribed mix is often likely to be significantly more expensive, in terms of materials used, than a concrete specified by its performance.

(4) Since the proportions of prescribed mixes relate to relatively poor-quality materials it is not possible to achieve reliable concretes of minimum strength greater than 30 N/mm² (about 4500 lbf/in²) at 28 days.

The circumstances under which a prescribed mix could be justified are:

(a) a very limited quantity of concrete, where the cost of a full mix design and trial mix are not justified;

(b) urgent work where there is no time to undertake a full mix design and trial mix; if the work, though urgently started, were to continue for a considerable time, data could be obtained from the early work, using the prescribed mix to justify a change to a designed mix a later date.

Both the above circumstances presuppose that the concrete will be batched and mixed at the construction site without the benefit of test data collected from previously produced concrete on that site. The position of the ready mixed concrete supplier is, however, rather different in that in most cases he is able to supply a designed mix to meet a performance specification. Thus a specifying authority generally specifies concrete to meet the performance requirements and should, whenever possible, permit the contractor to use a prescribed mix where one has been previously agreed or published in a Code of Practice or other suitable document. In this way the specifying authority is more likely to obtain the most economical concrete for the work in hand; in effect, the contractor will assess the relative costs of using either site mixing of a designed mix (accepting the cost in time and money of a full mix design, together with the cost of testing), or site mixing of a prescribed mix (accepting a possible increase in the cost of materials), or ready mixed concrete.

It is generally accepted that, for designed mixes, the quality of concrete should be assessed by taking samples of the concrete at frequent intervals and testing for workability and strength. The results of the tests may be used to help in maintaining good control of uniformity or to judge whether or not the concrete has complied with the specification. The position regarding prescribed mixes is, however, less clear. If the specifying authority has specified a prescribed mix, then, logically, once the intended prescribed values have been met, no further test is required unless it is intended to collect data to justify a subsequent change to a designed mix. On the other hand, if the specifying authority has specified the concrete in terms of performance and has subsequently agreed to a contractor's request to use a prescribed mix, then it is not unreasonable for the specifying authority to insist upon the testing requirements originally specified.

2.2 Nominal mixes

Reference must be made to the specification of concrete by nominal volumetric mix proportions as these are still widely used despite the well-known weaknesses of such a form of specification.[10] Originally the proportions were, in effect, a prescription of the proportions of cement : fine aggregate : coarse aggregate in terms of the bulk volumes of the individual materials. The wide variations found in the bulk density of cement soon led to the general adoption of batching cement by the bag, which is taken as 50 kg (112 lb). In order that the quantities of aggregate may be determined, this quantity of Portland cement can be taken to have a bulk volume of 35 dm^3 (1.25 ft^3); that is, the bulk density of Portland cement is about 1450 kg/m^3 (90 lb/ft^3).

The bulk volume of high alumina cement is the same as that for Portland cement, whereas that of nominally 50 kg bags of supersulphated cement is taken as 45 dm^3 (1.6 ft^3), corresponding to a bulk density of about 1100 kg/m^3 (70 lb/ft^3). (1 dm^3 = 0.001 m^3 = 1 litre.)

Experience also showed that allowance had to be made for the bulking which occurs with fine aggregates when they are damp; it is generally accepted that most concreting sands will bulk on average by about 25%. However, coarse aggregates do not bulk to any significant extent. The allowance can be increased for finer sands and decreased if the moisture content of the sand is unusually low

Taking, as an example, a mix of nominal volumetric proportions of 1 : 2 : 4, the batch quantities can be calculated as

Portland cement	1 bag
Dry sand	2 x 35 = 70 dm^3 or, more conveniently, $70 \times \dfrac{125}{100} = 87.5$ dm^3 (3.1 ft^3) of damp sand
Coarse aggregate	4 x 35 = 140 dm^3 (5 ft^3)

An adjustment of the proportion of fine to coarse aggregate is often permitted to the extent that the ratio of the two can vary between 1 : 2 and 1 : 1½. This enables the proportion of fine aggregate to be increased if it has an unusually coarse grading or if the concrete is of high workability. The total quantity of aggregate to cement should not be altered.

If it is required to use all-in or reconstituted aggregate (see Chapter 3.2.3) rather than separate fine and coarse aggregates, then the volume of all-in aggregate will be about 170 dm^3 (6 ft^3) and not 70 + 140 = 210 dm^3 (7.4 ft^3), as allowance must be made for the greater bulk density of all-in material than either fine or coarse material separately.

In the above discussion it will be noted that no mention is made of the proportion of water to be used. In practice this is judged so as to give a concrete of suitable workability for the work in hand. The fact that the required amount of water affects the final properties of the concrete very considerably, and that the quantity varies with both the selected workability of the concrete and the maximum size of the aggregate, shows the extreme weakness and the imprecision of this type of specification.

In practice, nominal volumetric mix proportions are often associated with a particular concrete strength which is checked by the taking of test specimens. This association of the prescription form of specification with a performance requirement leads to a difficult and often unworkable specification. Consequently, specifications for concrete based on the volumetric proportions of the constituents are to be deprecated.

Figure 2.1 provides a means whereby nominal volumetric proportions may be related to the aggregate/cement ratio by weight, which involves a knowledge of aggregate bulk densities, and to the cement content, which further involves a knowledge of the aggregate specific gravity and the water/cement ratio.

2.3 Standard mixes

Standard mixes have been introduced into Codes of Practice CP 114 and 116 partly as a replacement for nominal volumetric proportions; they may be used to produce three grades of concrete in which the specified works cube strengths at 28 days are 21, 25.5 and 30 N/mm^2 (3000, 3750 and 4500 lbf/in^2), with a proportion of test results below the specified value permitted to average 2.5%. The proportions are given entirely by weight and, for the convenience of using whole bags of cement, are based on the weight of one bag. The data given take account of the maximum size of the aggregate and the workability of the concrete and also of the aggregate particle shape and grading.

Data given in CP 116 are reproduced, with editorial modifications, in Table 2.2 which applies to two standards of quality control represented by standard deviations of 3.5 N/mm^2 (500 lbf/in^2) and 7 N/mm^2 (1000 lbf/in^2). This is to take account of the situation applying in precast concrete factories where the standard of quality control is likely to be known and therefore interpolation (not extrapolation) between the data for the two standards of quality control is permitted. In CP 114, however, the data are limited to one standard of control – 7 N/mm^2 (1000 lbf/in^2) – because it is unlikely that the standard of quality control will be known in advance for site-mixed concrete. The numerical values in CP 114 are the same as those given in CP 116 for the higher standard deviation.

Standard mixes apply only to concrete made with ordinary or rapid-hardening Portland cements complying with BS 12 or with Portland blastfurnace cement complying with BS 146, and with natural aggregates complying with BS 882 (except that fine aggregate to grading zone 4 is not allowed) or with air-cooled blastfurnace slag coarse aggregate complying with BS 1047. Air-entraining admixtures should not be used.

The weights given in Table 2.2 are based on the use of a sand of grading zone 2 as described in BS 882. If a crushed stone sand or a crushed gravel sand is used, the weight of coarse aggregate should be reduced by at least 10 kg (25 lb).

9

TABLE 2.2 (metric units)
Standard mixes. weights of fine and coarse aggregate per bag of cement for various minimum strengths of concrete.

Standard deviation – N/mm²	Minimum strength of concrete at 28 days – N/mm²	Weight of dry sand – kg	Weight of dry gravel or crushed rock coarse aggregate – kg											
			10 mm maximum size			14 mm maximum size			20 mm maximum size			40 mm maximum size		
Workability Slump – mm Compacting factor			Low 0-5 0.80-0.86	Medium 5-25 0.86-0.92	High 25-50 0.92-0.97	Low 5-20 0.81-0.87	Medium 20-40 0.87-0.93	High 40-100 0.93-0.97	Low 12-25 0.82-0.88	Medium 25-50 0.88-0.94	High 50-125 0.94-0.97	Low 25-50 0.82-0.88	Medium 50-100 0.88-0.94	High 100-175 0.94-0.97
3.5	21	135	155	125	100	180	145	125	200	165	145	*	*	190
	25.5	110	155	125	100	180	145	125	200	165	145	*	200	180
	30	90	145	110	90	165	135	110	190	155	135	225	190	165
7.0	21	90	145	110	90	165	135	110	190	155	135	225	190	165
	25.5	80	125	90	65	145	110	90	165	135	110	200	165	145
	30	65	100	*	*	125	90	*	145	110	90	165	135	110

* indicates the mix would have a cement content outside the range 240 to 540 kg/m³.

TABLE 2.2 (imperial units)
Standard mixes: weights of fine and coarse aggregate per bag of cement for various minimum strengths of concrete.

Standard deviation – lbf/in²	Minimum strength of concrete at 28 days – lbf/in²	Weight of dry sand – lb	Weight of dry gravel or crushed rock coarse aggregate – lb											
			3/8 in. maximum size			½ in. maximum size			¾ in. maximum size			1½ in. maximum size		
Workability Slump – in. Compacting factor			Low 0-¼ 0.80-0.86	Medium ¼-1 0.86-0.92	High 1-2 0.92-0.97	Low ¼-¾ 0.81-0.87	Medium ¾-1½ 0.87-0.93	High 1½-4 0.93-0.97	Low ½-1 0.82-0.88	Medium 1-2 0.88-0.94	High 2-5 0.94-0.97	Low 1-2 0.82-0.88	Medium 2-4 0.88-0.94	High 4-7 0.94-0.97
500	3000	300	350	275	225	400	325	275	450	375	325	*	*	425
	3750	250	350	275	225	400	325	275	450	375	325	*	450	400
	4500	200	325	250	200	375	300	250	425	350	300	500	425	375
1000	3000	200	325	250	200	375	300	250	425	350	300	500	425	375
	3750	175	275	200	150	325	250	200	375	300	250	450	375	325
	4500	150	225	*	*	275	200	*	325	250	200	375	300	250

* indicates the mix would have a cement content outside the range 400 to 900 lb/yd³.

The weight of fine aggregate should be reduced by at least 10 kg (25 lb) if its grading is within the limits of zone 3 of BS 882 and should be increased by at least 10 kg (25 lb) if its grading is within the limits of grading zone 1. There should be a corresponding increase or decrease respectively in the weight of coarse aggregate to maintain the same total weight of aggregate.

If the specific gravity of either the coarse or fine aggregate differs significantly from 2.6, which was assumed when the data were compiled, the weight of each type of aggregate should be adjusted in proportion to the specific gravity of that material.

2.4 Prescribed mixes

Prescribed mixes have been introduced into CP 110 and include a wide range of characteristic concrete strengths from 7 N/mm² (1000 lbf/in²) to 30 N/mm² (4350 lbf/in²) at 28 days. These are given in Table 2.3. The quantities of materials are given entirely by weight to add up as nearly as possible to 1 m³ (1 yd³) of concrete; should the quantities not add up to this volume, due to a difference in specific gravity between the job aggregate and the value of 2.7 assumed for the aggregate in the calculation of the quantities in Table 2.3, then, strictly speaking, the quantity of

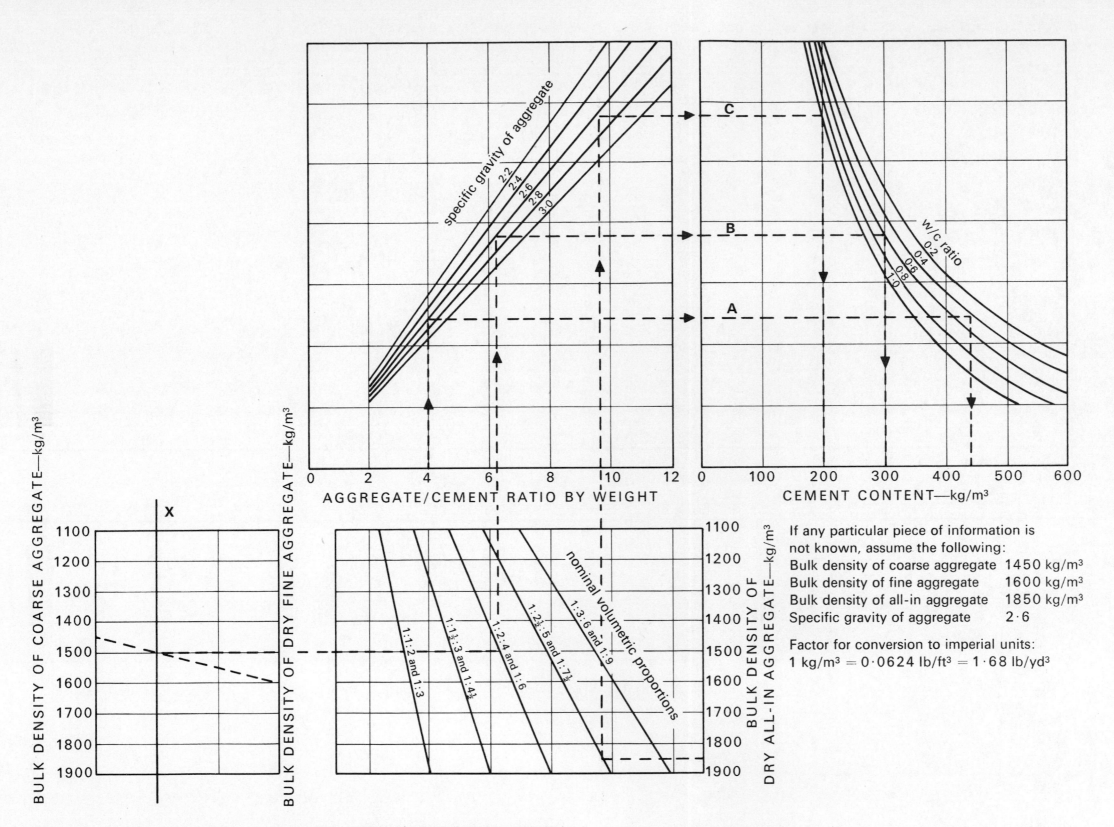

Figure 2.1 : Conversion of nominal volumetric mix proportions to aggregate/cement ratios and cement contents.

Three examples are shown to illustrate ways in which this chart may be used. The densities given above are assumed in every case.

(1) The conversion of a mix of aggregate/cement ratio 4 with a water/cement ratio of 0.4 to a cement content of 440 kg/m³, shown as broken line *A*.

(2) The conversion of a nominal 1 : 2 : 4 mix by volume with a water/cement ratio of 0.6 to a cement content of 300 kg/m³. Start by joining the bulk densities of coarse and fine aggregates, and where the line crosses line *X* work through the graphs as shown by broken line *B*.

(3) The conversion of a nominal 1 : 7.5 mix by volume with a water/cement ratio of 1.0 to a cement content of 200 kg/m³, shown as broken line *C*.

TABLE 2.3 (metric units)
Prescribed mixes for ordinary structural concrete. Weights of cement and total dry aggregates in kg to produce approximately one cubic metre of fully compacted concrete, together with the percentages by weight of fine aggregate in total dry aggregates.

Characteristic strength at 28 days – N/mm²	Workability	Nominal maximum size of aggregate – mm							
		40		20		14		10	
		Medium	High	Medium	High	Medium	High	Medium	High
	Slump – mm	50-100	100-150	25-75	75-125	10-50	50-100	10-25	25-50
7	Cement – kg	180	200	210	230	–	–	–	–
	Total aggregate – kg	1950	1850	1900	1800	–	–	–	–
	Fine aggregate – %	30-45	30-45	35-50	35-50	–	–	–	–
10	Cement – kg	210	230	240	260	–	–	–	–
	Total aggregate – kg	1900	1850	1850	1800	–	–	–	–
	Fine aggregate – %	30-45	30-45	35-50	35-50	–	–	–	–
15	Cement – kg	250	270	280	310	–	–	–	–
	Total aggregate – kg	1850	1800	1800	1750	–	–	–	–
	Fine aggregate – %	30-45	30-45	35-50	35-50	–	–	–	–
20	Cement – kg	300	320	320	350	340	380	360	410
	Total aggregate – kg	1850	1750	1800	1750	1750	1700	1750	1650
	Sand*								
	Zone 1 – %	35	40	40	45	45	50	50	55
	Zone 2 – %	30	35	35	40	40	45	45	50
	Zone 3 – %	30	30	30	35	35	40	40	45
25	Cement – kg	340	360	360	390	380	420	400	450
	Total aggregate – kg	1800	1750	1750	1700	1700	1650	1700	1600
	Sand*								
	Zone 1 – %	35	40	40	45	45	50	50	55
	Zone 2 – %	30	35	35	40	40	45	45	50
	Zone 3 – %	30	30	30	35	35	40	40	45
30	Cement – kg	370	390	400	430	430	470	460	510
	Total aggregate – kg	1750	1700	1700	1650	1700	1600	1650	1550
	Sand*								
	Zone 1 – %	35	40	40	45	45	50	50	55
	Zone 2 – %	30	35	35	40	40	45	45	50
	Zone 3 – %	30	30	30	35	35	40	40	45

* Sand is fine aggregate resulting from the natural disintegration of rock.

aggregate batched should be adjusted accordingly. The data given take account of the maximum size of the aggregate, the workability of the concrete and the grading of the fine aggregate, in such a way that all combinations give sensibly the same water/cement ratio at each level of strength.

The standard of control assumed is represented by a margin between the characteristic strength and the target mean strength of two-thirds of the characteristic strength, where the characteristic strength is 15 N/mm² (2200 lbf/in²) or below, and of 15 N/mm² where the characteristic strength is 20, 25 or 30 N/mm² (2900, 3600 or 4350 lbf/in²). These values have been selected as representing the poorest standard likely to occur on site, though it is possible this margin could be shown to be inadequate in very extreme cases.

Prescribed mixes apply only to concrete made with ordinary or rapid-hardening Portland cement complying with BS 12 or with Portland blastfurnace cement com-plying with BS 146 or with sulphate-resisting Portland cement complying with BS 4027, and with natural aggregates complying with BS 882 (except that crushed fine aggregate and fine aggregate to grading zone 4 of BS 882 should not be used) or with air-cooled blastfurnace slag coarse aggregate complying with BS 1047. Prescribed mixes can be used under the appropriate durability conditions of Tables 5.2, 5.3 and 5.4 provided the conditions of these tables can be met; for this purpose the free water/cement ratios of prescribed mixes of characteristic strengths 20, 25 and 30 N/mm² can be taken as 0.55, 0.50 and 0.45 respectively. Air-entraining admixtures should not be used with prescribed mixes, and therefore prescribed mixes should not be used to meet the air entrainment conditions in Table 5.2.

The data in Table 2.3 are reproduced in Table 2.4, where quantities are based on the use of whole bags of cement.

TABLE 2.3 (imperial units)
Prescribed mixes for ordinary structural concrete. Weights of cement and total dry aggregates in lb to produce approximately one cubic yard of fully compacted concrete, together with the percentages by weight of fine aggregate in total dry aggregates.

Characteristic strength at 28 days – lbf/in^2		Nominal maximum size of aggregate – in.							
		1½		¾		½		3/8	
	Workability	Medium	High	Medium	High	Medium	High	Medium	High
	Slump – in.	2-4	4-6	1-3	3-5	½-2	2-4	½-1	1-2
1000	Cement – lb	300	340	350	390	–	–	–	–
	Total aggregate - lb	3300	3100	3200	3050	–	–	–	–
	Fine aggregate – %	30-45	30-45	35-50	35-50	–	–	–	–
1450	Cement – lb	350	390	400	440	–	–	–	–
	Total aggregate – lb	3200	3100	3100	3050	–	–	–	–
	Fine aggregate – %	30-45	30-45	35-50	35-50	–	–	–	–
2200	Cement – lb	420	460	470	520	–	–	–	–
	Total aggregate – lb	3100	3050	3050	2950	–	–	–	–
	Fine aggregate – %	30-45	30-45	35-50	35-50	–	–	–	–
2900	Cement – lb	500	540	540	590	570	640	610	690
	Total aggregate – lb	3100	2950	3050	2950	2950	2850	2950	2800
	Sand*								
	Zone 1 – %	35	40	40	45	45	50	50	55
	Zone 2 – %	30	35	35	40	40	45	45	50
	Zone 3 – %	30	30	30	35	35	40	40	45
3600	Cement – lb	570	610	610	660	640	710	670	760
	Total aggregate – lb	3050	2950	2950	2850	2850	2800	2850	2700
	Sand*								
	Zone 1 – %	35	40	40	45	45	50	50	55
	Zone 2 – %	30	35	35	40	40	45	45	50
	Zone 3 – %	30	30	30	35	35	40	40	45
4350	Cement – lb	620	660	670	720	720	790	780	860
	Total aggregate – lb	2950	2850	2850	2800	2850	2700	2800	2600
	Sand*								
	Zone 1 – %	35	40	40	45	45	50	50	55
	Zone 2 – %	30	35	35	40	40	45	45	50
	Zone 3 – %	30	30	30	35	35	40	40	45

*Sand is fine aggregate resulting from the natural disintegration of rock.

2.5 Rationalized road mixes

The principle of the prescribed mix has been extended to cover concrete used for the wearing course in roads and other paved areas.[11] The principal difference from other forms of prescription is that the concrete for roads should be air-entrained (see Chapter 3.4.6). Thus an air-entraining admixture should be added at a dosage shown by site trials to give the correct quantity of air. It is advisable to undertake regular and frequent testing of the concrete on site for air content, workability and strength, though the latter would be for guidance and not form a specification requirement. As with other forms of prescribed mix, the mixing water should be added to give the intended workability, which has been fixed so as to be suitable for semi-manual construction techniques using a vibrating tamper, and for mechanized construction using the machines currently available.

The proportions of rationalized road mixes given in Table 2.5 are associated with a characteristic strength of 30 N/mm^2 (4350 lbf/in^2) and a margin of 15 N/mm^2 (2200 lbf/in^2) (see Chapter 4.2) and apply generally to Portland cement complying with BS 12 or Portland blastfurnace cement complying with BS 146. The aggregate should be of 20 mm (¾ in.) or 40 mm (1½ in.) nominal maximum size and should comply with BS 882, except that neither limestone fine aggregate (natural or crushed) nor fine aggregate to grading zone 4 should be used. The air-entraining admixture should be of the neutralized wood resin or other appropriate type and should be added at such a rate as to produce an air content of 4.5 ± 1.5% determined in accordance with BS 1881, Part 2, Clause 6. The workability of the concrete for semi-manual construction methods should be such that the average slump is between 15 mm (½ in.) and 40 mm (1½ in.), or that the average compacting factor is between 0.85 and 0.90. Where concrete is being placed by machine, the workability should be towards the lower end of this range.

TABLE 2.4
Prescribed mixes based on a bag of cement. Weights of aggregate required to one bag of ordinary Portland cement, together with the percentages by weight of fine aggregate in total dry aggregate.

METRIC UNITS

Characteristic strength at 28 days – N/mm²	Workability	Maximum size of aggregate – mm							
		40		20		14		10	
		Medium	High	Medium	High	Medium	High	Medium	High
	Slump – mm	50-100	100-150	25-75	75-125	10-50	50-100	10-25	25-50
7	Total aggregate – kg	535	465	450	395	–	–	–	–
	Fine aggregate – %	30-45	30-45	35-50	35-50	–	–	–	–
10	Total aggregate – kg	455	400	385	345	–	–	–	–
	Fine aggregate – %	30-45	30-45	35-50	35-50	–	–	–	–
15	Total aggregate – kg	375	335	325	280	–	–	–	–
	Fine aggregate – %	30-45	30-45	35-50	35-50	–	–	–	–
20	Total aggregate – kg	305	275	280	245	260	225	240	200
	Sand* – %								
	Zone 1	35	40	40	45	45	50	50	55
	Zone 2	30	35	35	40	40	45	45	50
	Zone 3	30	30	30	35	35	40	40	45
25	Total aggregate – kg	265	240	245	215	225	200	210	180
	Sand* – %								
	Zone 1	35	40	40	45	45	50	50	55
	Zone 2	30	35	35	40	40	45	45	50
	Zone 3	30	30	30	35	35	40	40	45
30	Total aggregate – kg	240	220	215	190	195	175	180	150
	Sand* – %								
	Zone 1	35	40	40	45	45	50	50	55
	Zone 2	30	35	35	40	40	45	45	50
	Zone 3	30	30	30	35	35	40	40	45

IMPERIAL UNITS

Characteristic strength at 28 days – lbf/in²	Workability	Maximum size of aggregate – in.							
		1½		¾		½		3/8	
		Medium	High	Medium	High	Medium	High	Medium	High
	Slump – in.	2-4	4-6	1-3	3-5	½-2	2-4	½-1	1-2
1000	Total aggregate – lb	1200	1040	1010	880	–	–	–	–
	Fine aggregate – %	30-45	30-45	35-50	35-50	–	–	–	–
1450	Total aggregate – lb	1020	900	860	770	–	–	–	–
	Fine aggregate – %	30-45	30-45	35-50	35-50	–	–	–	–
2200	Total aggregate – lb	840	750	730	630	–	–	–	–
	Fine aggregate – %	30-45	30-45	35-50	35-50	–	–	–	–
2900	Total aggregate – lb	680	620	630	550	580	500	540	450
	Sand* – %								
	Zone 1	35	40	40	45	45	50	50	55
	Zone 2	30	35	35	40	40	45	45	50
	Zone 3	30	30	30	35	35	40	40	45
3600	Total aggregate – lb	590	540	550	480	500	450	470	400
	Sand* – %								
	Zone 1	35	40	40	45	45	50	50	55
	Zone 2	30	35	35	40	40	45	45	50
	Zone 3	30	30	30	35	35	40	40	45
4350	Total aggregate – lb	540	490	480	430	440	390	400	340
	Sand* – %								
	Zone 1	35	40	40	45	45	50	50	55
	Zone 2	30	35	35	40	40	45	45	50
	Zone 3	30	30	30	35	35	40	40	45

* Sand is fine aggregate resulting from the natural disintegration of rock.

TABLE 2.5
Rationalized road mixes.

(a) Preferred specification

| | | Cement content of fully compacted concrete — kg/m³ (lb/yd³) | Approximate proportion of fine aggregate in total aggregate —% | | |
| | | | Natural sand grading zone | | |
			1	2	3
Maximum size of coarse	20 (¾)	380 (640)	45	40	35
aggregate — mm (in.)	40 (1½)	340 (570)	40	35	30

(b) Alternative specification

		Dry weight of aggregate per bag of cement — kg (lb)					
		Natural sand grading zone					
		1		2		3	
		fine	coarse	fine	coarse	fine	coarse
Maximum size of coarse	20 (¾)	110 (240)	130 (290)	100 (210)	140 (320)	80 (180)	160 (350)
aggregate — mm (in.)	40 (1½)	110 (240)	170 (380)	100 (210)	180 (400)	80 (180)	200 (430)

Notes
(1) The proportion of fine to coarse aggregate may require slight adjustment to attain the most suitable workability although, under the alternative specification, the total weight of aggregate should not be increased.

(2) If crushed rock is used as fine aggregate, a richer mix may be necessary to maintain strength and the proportion of fine aggregate may have to be higher to attain the most suitable workability; designed mixes should therefore be used.

(3) These mixes are based on the assumption that the concrete is subject to good control.

CHAPTER 3

Concrete constituents

3.1 Cements[12-14]

3.1.1 General

The vast majority of the cement used in construction work is described as being a Portland cement, and it is with this general type that most of this book is concerned. The other types discussed are high alumina cement and super-sulphated cement.

All Portland cements have the same chemical constituents, and it is the variation in the relative proportions of these chemicals which determines the individual type of cement. Most Portland cement used is ordinary Portland and, for this type, the relative proportions of the constituents are selected to provide a cement suitable for a very wide range of applications.

Portland cements are manufactured by mixing calcareous or other lime-containing material with argillaceous or other material containing silica, alumina or iron oxide, burning them at a high temperature to produce a clinker, and grinding the clinker to a fine powder with a small proportion of gypsum. The principal chemical constituents formed are tricalcium silicate, dicalcium silicate, tricalcium aluminate and tetracalcium aluminoferrite, often abbreviated to C_3S, C_2S, C_3A and C_4AF respectively; of these, the first two are particularly important because they provide the cementing action — the higher the proportion of C_3S relative to the C_2S, the more quickly strength is gained after mixing. The quantity of gypsum added controls the process of setting and hardening of the cement, which is a chemical combination with water known as hydration. Thus, the finer the cement particles, the greater the surface area of the cement available for hydration, and consequently the more rapid and the more complete is the reaction. The finer cement is ground, therefore, the greater is the early strength developed. Fineness is generally measured in terms of the specific surface of the cement determined in an air permeability apparatus; a typical value for ordinary Portland cement would be 300 m^2/kg.

Hydration of cement starts from the time water is added and the gain in strength is accompanied by an increasing stiffness of the mixture. Cement specifications include the measurement of the extent of stiffening, or setting time, by an arbitrary test procedure, and require the setting time to fall within prescribed limits. This ensures that the cement paste, or the concrete made with the cement, does not stiffen unduly quickly or slowly. It is worth observing, however, that although particular setting times may be obtained from tests on cement paste, the same times do not apply to concrete made with the same cement; in general, concrete will take substantially longer to stiffen.

Hardened cement pastes which are allowed to dry out show a slight permanent shrinkage, whereas those which are kept in water expand slightly. Such movements are a normal property of good cement. However, if the proportion of lime used in the manufacture of the cement were more than could combine with the other constituents present, the surplus would remain in the cement as a crystallized hard-burnt lime which would hydrate very slowly over a period of months or years to an extent that might disrupt the concrete. Such cements are described as being unsound, and cement specifications include a test procedure for detecting them. In practice unsound cements are nowadays virtually unknown and the test is largely a historical relic.

The hydration of cement is an exothermic chemical reaction, the amount of heat generated ranging from less than 250 to over 420 kj/kg of cement. This heat develops rapidly in the first few days after the concrete is mixed, and more slowly thereafter, to reach, typically, a total value of about 350 kj/kg for ordinary Portland cement after 28 days. The heat can result in an undesirably high rise in temperature in large masses of concrete, with steep temperature gradients between the centre and the surface of the concrete; when the concrete finally cools it may exhibit thermal cracking. On the other hand, the heat is often of considerable benefit in cold weather. It should be noted that the development of heat, which tends to be higher for cements having a higher tricalcium aluminate content, is associated with — though not directly proportional to — the development of strength, and therefore some compromise between conflicting requirements may have to be made in some mix designs for concrete to be cast in large masses.

3.1.2 Rapid-hardening Portland cement

As the name implies, rapid-hardening Portland cement is so manufactured as to gain strength rather more rapidly than ordinary cement in the first few days after mixing. The chemical composition is generally similar, perhaps with a slightly higher proportion of tricalcium silicate to dicalcium silicate, and the cement is ground a little finer. Apart from the higher early strength and a slightly greater rate of development of heat of hydration, concrete made with rapid-hardening cement is similar to that made with ordinary cement.

Where concrete is required to reach a particular strength at an age of about 7 days or less, it may prove worth while using a rapid-hardening as against an ordinary cement. Examples include pre-tensioned prestressed concrete and situations involving the need to strike formwork early, to open a road to traffic more quickly, or to offset the adverse effects of low temperatures during winter building.

3.1.3 Extra-rapid-hardening cement

Extra-rapid-hardening cement is made by intergrinding a small amount of calcium chloride with rapid-hardening cement. The result is that the hydration of the cement is considerably accelerated, leading to faster stiffening of the concrete, higher early strengths and a higher rate of development of heat of hydration. The cement is particularly suitable for cold-weather concreting, though it can be used in more normal temperatures for urgent work, in which case the concrete should be placed and compacted within about 30 minutes of the end of mixing because of the rapid rate of stiffening. Due to the fact that calcium chloride increases the risk of corrosion of embedded steel, particularly where the quantity of anhydrous calcium chloride exceeds 1.5% by weight of cement, this type of cement is not recommended for reinforced or prestressed concrete (see also Chapter 3.4.5).

3.1.4 Ultra-high early strength cement

A recent development has been the production of a cement capable of producing very high strengths at an early age without the incorporation of calcium chloride. The cement has a fineness typically of 700 to 800 m^2/kg.

3.1.5 Portland blastfurnace cement

Portland blastfurnace cement is made by grinding a mixture of ordinary Portland cement with not more than about twice, and generally half, the weight of granulated blast-furnace slag. The properties of the cement are very similar to those of ordinary Portland cement, though it gains strength rather more slowly at early ages.

3.1.6 Low heat Portland cement

The principal property distinguishing low heat cement from ordinary cement is the considerably lower heat of hydration brought about by limiting the tricalcium silicate and tricalcium aluminate content of the cement. The heat of hydration at 28 days is specified to be below 290 kj/kg, as against the typical 350 kj/kg for ordinary cement. The rate of early strength development is also lower, though somewhat similar values of final strength are obtained.

Low heat Portland cement is moderately sulphate-resisting due to the generally low tricalcium aluminate content, though the resistance does not reach the standard of sulphate-resisting Portland cement in this respect.

Low heat cement is of particular value in the construction of large masses of concrete, where the heat generated by the cement might otherwise result in excessively high temperatures being reached in the concrete in the first few days after casting. The low rate of gain of strength is not likely to be a disadvantage in most mass concrete work. Due to the low rate of development of heat, the cement is not suitable for cold-weather work unless particularly careful precautions are taken against freezing of the concrete during the first few days after casting.

3.1.7 Low heat Portland blastfurnace cement

The rate of gain of strength of low heat Portland blast-furnace cement is similar to that of low heat Portland cement but is less than that of Portland blastfurnace cement. As the name suggests, blastfurnace slag is interground into the cement to constitute between 50 and 90% of the cement by weight. The cement should be used in the same way, and in the same circumstances, as low heat cement.

3.1.8 Sulphate-resisting Portland cement

The use of sulphate-resisting cement has greatly extended in recent years since research and site observation have shown that concrete made with a cement similar in most respects to ordinary Portland cement, but containing less than 3.5% tricalcium aluminate, shows considerably greater resistance to attack by aggressive sulphate solutions in ground water or soil. Details of the use of the cement are discussed in Chapter 5.

3.1.9 White and coloured Portland cements

White Portland cement is made by using china clay instead of ordinary clay during manufacture; this is done to exclude impurities and particularly iron oxide which is primarily responsible for the grey colour of normal cement. The properties of white cement are otherwise similar to those of ordinary Portland cement. The principal use is for architectural and decorative effects. Considerable care is needed to ensure the concrete is not contaminated by coloured materials during batching, mixing, placing or curing.

Coloured Portland cements are made by adding up to 10% of pigments to white cement to produce pale shades, or to ordinary Portland cement when deeper colours are required.

3.1.10 Hydrophobic cement

Hydrophobic cement has been developed to prevent partial hydration of the cement during storage, especially in damp conditions. A water-repellent film is coated round each grain of cement by intergrinding suitable materials, such as oleic acid, lauric acid or stearic acid with the clinker during the production of the cement. During mixing of the concrete the protective film is rubbed off by the aggregate, and hydration of the cement proceeds normally. For this reason, thorough mixing is needed. The freshly mixed concrete generally has good workability and contains about 1% of entrained air. The hardened concrete retains the water-repellent characteristics of the cement but is otherwise similar to ordinary Portland cement concrete.

3.1.11   Water-repellent cement

Several types of Portland cement are produced which contain an interground water-repellent material. This cement can be used to produce a water-repellent concrete, the properties of which are more fully discussed in Chapter 3.4.10.

3.1.12   High alumina cement

High alumina cement is made from a source of lime, such as limestone or chalk, and a source of alumina, such as bauxite, which is aluminium oxide usually containing impurities of iron oxides, titanium and small amounts of silica. In manufacture the bauxite and limestone are often crushed into lumps about 100 mm (4 in.) across, fed into a furnace fired with pulverized coal, and heated to a temperature of about 1600°C. Fusion takes place and the molten material is allowed to cool and is then ground to a fineness of 250 to 320 m²/kg. The main cementitious compounds are calcium aluminates.

The principal advantages of using high alumina cement as against ordinary Portland cement are a very high early strength, an increased resistance in the hardened concrete to attack by sulphates and some acids, and good refractory properties. Against this, the rate of heat evolution is very high at early ages. There is a risk of conversion under some circumstances, and the cement is relatively expensive. Particular aspects of the use of high alumina cement are discussed in Chapter 6.1.7.

High alumina cement should not be mixed with other cements, calcium chloride admixtures, or sea water.

3.1.13   Supersulphated cement

Supersulphated cement is made by intergrinding a mixture of 80 to 85% of granulated slag, 10 to 15% of calcium sulphate and about 5% of Portland cement clinker to a fineness of 400 to 500 m²/kg. The cement is particularly sensitive to poor storage conditions before use and can therefore deteriorate.

Concrete made with supersulphated cement has a good resistance to almost all the concentrations of sulphate normally found in ground water or soil and even exhibits some resistance in mildly acidic conditions. The heat of hydration of supersulphated cement is low, typically reaching 190 to 210 kj/kg at 28 days. For this reason, particular care has to be taken, when using the cement in cold weather, to prevent the concrete freezing; it does not harden well under about 8°C. The concrete also requires particularly good curing for the first four days after casting to prevent the surface from becoming powdery.

Supersulphated cement should not be mixed with any other cements.

3.1.14   Selection of type of cement

It is difficult to generalize on the properties of concretes made with different types of cement, though an approximate guide is given in Table 3.1, from which it is possible to select particular cements where a high early strength, a low early rate of evolution of heat of hydration or resistance to sulphate attack is required. In addition to this comparison, it should be borne in mind that the properties of a concrete containing any one type of cement can be varied widely, depending on the mix design; for example, a careful mix design using ordinary Portland cement might well reduce the heat of hydration developed in a mass concrete section to the extent that a special low heat cement becomes unnecessary.

3.1.15   Specification of cement

In most instances it is sufficient to specify cement by reference to the appropriate British Standard Specification as listed in Table 3.1. Where a British Standard does not exist, the cement should comply with BS 12 so far as is possible.

3.2   Aggregates[2, 4, 15]

3.2.1   General

Aggregates comprise between about 60 and 75% of the total volume of concrete, and therefore careful consideration must always be given to the properties of the aggregate which greatly affect all the important properties of concrete in construction work. Since aggregate is relatively inexpensive it is generally economic to arrange to use as a high a proportion of it in the concrete as possible. The inclusion of aggregate, however, also improves several of the properties of the hardened concrete; for example, it reduces drying shrinkage.

Although aggregate is often thought of as being merely a filler in concrete, this is not correct since the aggregate can impart some of its own properties, at least partially, to the concrete; for example, the coefficient of thermal expansion of the aggregate has a major effect on the coefficient for the concrete as a whole.

TABLE 3.1
An approximate guide to the relative properties of concrete made with different types of cement, in comparison with concrete made with ordinary Portland cement. The mixes are assumed to contain 300 kg of cement per m³ (500 lb/yd³).

Types of cement	Setting characteristics at normal temperatures*	Strength development			Early rate of evolution of heat of hydration	Resistance to sulphate attack
		1 to 2 days	about 7 days	about 28 days		
Portland cements						
rapid-hardening (BS 12)	similar	~ 50-75% more	~ 15% more	similar	higher	similar
blastfurnace (BS 146)	perhaps slightly slower	similar	similar	similar	slightly lower	slightly better
low heat (BS 1370)	slightly slower	~ 50% less	~ 30% less	slightly lower	considerably lower	similar
sulphate-resisting (BS 4027)	similar	similar	similar	similar	perhaps slightly lower	considerably better
low heat blastfurnace (BS 4246)	slightly slower	~ 50% less	~ 30% less	slightly lower	considerably lower	slightly better
extra-rapid-hardening	generally, ½-1 h	~ 100% more	~ 20% more	similar	considerably higher	similar
ultra-high early strength	faster	over 100% more	~ 40% more	slightly higher	considerably higher	similar
white and coloured (BS 12)	similar	perhaps slightly less	perhaps slightly less	similar	similar	similar
water-repellent	similar	similar	similar	similar	similar	similar
hydrophobic	similar	similar	similar	similar	similar	similar
Other types						
high alumina (BS 915)	similar to OPC	full working strength developed within 2 days	—	—	very considerably greater than OPC	very considerably better than OPC
super-sulphated (BS 4248)	perhaps slightly slower than OPC	slightly lower than OPC	similar to OPC	similar to OPC	considerably lower than OPC	considerably better than OPC

* Concrete made with ordinary Portland cement sets in 2 to 8 hours, depending on mix proportions.

3.2.2 Types of aggregate

Aggregates are generally composed of naturally occurring gravel, rock and sand, though an increasing number of synthetic materials are being used, for example, to produce concretes of lower density than is obtained with natural materials.

A classification of natural aggregates can be made petrologically. Whilst this classification does not distinguish between those materials which are and are not suitable for concrete, the petrological group can give an indication of some of the likely properties of the concrete. Thus there are a few occasions where it would be appropriate to select aggregate of a particular petrological group for special work. The principal types used in the United Kingdom are as follows.

Basalt, granite and porphyry (BS 882 and 1201)
Materials from these groups can be used for almost all concreting uses. They are often associated with concretes of high strength, high abrasion resistance and good resistance to slipping and skidding. The concretes are reasonably easy to saw. The aggregates weather well and are often used for exposed aggregate work.

Limestone (BS 882 and 1201)
Although limestone varies widely in quality and strength of stone, carefully selected sources of material have been used very successfully for most types of concrete work. Particular advantages of limestone aggregate concrete include a relatively good resistance to fire and a low coefficient of thermal expansion; the concrete is one of the easiest to saw. The aggregate is, however, likely to produce a concrete of lower than average resistance to slipping and skidding, though it does not necessarily have to be discounted on these grounds.

Limestone, like cement paste, can react with several aggressive agencies including peaty (acidic) ground waters and some 'soft' (neutral or acidic) waters containing significant quantities of dissolved free carbon dioxide. Where there is doubt about the use of limestone aggregate concrete in ground waters, the water should be analysed for hardness and free carbon dioxide and its pH value determined. Generally, water classified under analysis as being 'hard' or of 'medium' hardness presents no difficulties. A few parts per million of dissolved carbon dioxide is similarly acceptable; perhaps the simplest way of distinguishing this is to say that water which is 'lime-precipitating' in character is acceptable and one which is 'lime-dissolving' could make a concrete which would be slowly eroded in service. However, these chemical effects are dependent on the porosity of the stone itself; a dense stone with a water absorption value below 2% would be much less likely to lead to deterioration than one having a higher absorption value.

A further and comparatively rare reaction, known as 'dedolomitization', can occur with certain magnesium limestones which have a high proportion of silica bound up in the crystal lattice. The silica can distort the lattice so that the soluble alkalis in the cement can penetrate the stone and chemically remove the magnesium. This is a form of alkali-aggregate reaction and presents the same problems as the more common form of alkali-aggregate reaction where the reactive part of the aggregate is silica. No magnesium limestone with less than 5% combined silica has ever been shown to be reactive in this way.

Flint (BS 882)
Flint is the basis of a very high proportion of gravel aggregates which may be won from land-based pits or from the sea. Flint gravels may be used for any concrete work, apart possibly from concretes of very high compressive strength, say 70 N/mm² (10 000 lbf/in²) or more. Flint gravel concretes are not so resistant to fire as limestone aggregate concretes, nor are they as easy to saw.

Blastfurnace slag (BS 1047)
Air-cooled blastfurnace slag is a by-product of the manufacture of pig-iron. Provided it complies with appropriate requirements for chemical composition, cleanliness and grading, it can be used as a coarse aggregate to make concrete of properties similar to those expected when natural dense aggregates are used.

Broken brick
Good-quality broken brick can be used as an aggregate in mass concrete where high degrees of impermeability and abrasion resistance are not required. The brick must be free from coatings of mortar, plaster or dust and should not contain soluble sulphates as SO_3 in excess of 0.5% by weight. Crushed brick has a generally better resistance to fire than most natural aggregates.

Lightweight aggregates [16-20]
A very wide range of lightweight aggregates is available for use in concrete where light weight or low thermal conductivity is required. The range of materials can best be considered in relation to the density of the aggregate. Some typical figures are given in Table 3.2.

Expanded polystyrene is an artificial organic material which is aerated to the extent of containing about 99% air. The material can be in the form of preformed beads or granulated foamed polystyrene.

Vermiculite is a material made from mica by heating to a temperature between 600°C and 900°C; it expands rapidly by exfoliation. It is used for insulation-grade concrete, though not for structural work.

TABLE 3.2
Air-dry densities (loose) of lightweight aggregates.

Aggregate type	Air-dry density – kg/m³ (lb/ft³)
expanded polystyrene	8-10 (0.5-0.6)
expanded vermiculite	60-160 (4-10)
expanded perlite	80-320 (5-20)
wood particles	320-480 (20-30)
diatomite	450-800 (28-50)
pumice	480-880 (30-55)
expanded slate (BS 3797) (Solite)	560-860 (35-54)
expanded shale (BS 3797) (Aglite)	320-960 (20-60)
expanded clay (BS 3797) (Leca)	320-960 (20-60)
foamed slag (BS 877)	560-960 (35-60)
sintered pulverized-fuel ash (BS 3797) (Lytag)	770-960 (48-60)
clinker (BS 1165)	720-1040 (45-65)

Perlite, a glassy volcanic rock, is imported from Italy. When rapidly heated to the point of fusion it expands to form a very light cellular material which is chiefly used in plastics; it has also been used for insulation-grade concrete, though not for structural concrete.

Graded wood particles can be treated with calcium chloride or lime or boiled in ferrous sulphate solution to remove tannin, soluble carbohydrates, wax and resin (which might affect the hydration of the cement) to make a further lightweight aggregate for use in concrete. The fact that the concrete can be nailed is one of its useful properties.

Diatomite is a natural material, calcined diatomaceous rock, which is formed from minute fossils of marine life and which is commercially available in the United Kingdom.

Pumice is a natural material of volcanic origin which has a cellular structure formed by bubbles of gas given off by molten lava during cooling. It is chemically inert and free from sulphur. Its lightweight and thermal insulation properties make it a good aggregate for such uses as concrete partition slabs, the encasement of steelwork and insulating screeds for roofs and floors.

Expanded slate, available under the trade name 'Solite', is produced by rapidly heating certain types of crushed slate in a carefully controlled rotary kiln to a temperature of about 1200°C. The gases generated change the laminar structure of the slate into a product containing a large number of minute cavities separated by glassy walls. After cooling, the slate is crushed and graded.

Expanded shale is manufactured by burning out and sintering colliery shale, which is a compressed form of clay, in a continuous furnace. The resulting clinker is then crushed and graded. Material is available under the trade name 'Aglite'.

Expanded clay, available under the trade name 'Leca', is formed when selected types of clay granules are heated until they are plastic and give off gases which swell them to several times their original volume. The process gives a honeycombed mass composed of minute cells divided by walls of vitrified material. Expanded clay coarse aggregate particles tend to be round in shape.

Foamed or expanded blastfurnace slag to BS 877 is produced by treating molten blastfurnace slag with a controlled quantity of water under certain conditions, so causing it to swell into a porous cellular structure which is substantially lighter than air-cooled slag.

Pulverized-fuel ash is formed in power stations using pulverized fuel and is the basis of a further lightweight material. An ash of suitable fineness and carbon content is selected and mixed with water and formed into pellets which are then fired at 1400°C. This causes the ash particles to coalesce without fully melting. The resulting lightweight aggregate is available under the trade name 'Lytag'.

Clinker (BS 1165) is the residue left after coal or coke has been completely burnt. It is important that clinker selected for use as an aggregate conforms to the test limits specified in BS 1165 for soluble sulphate content and loss on ignition because, if the combustion has not been completed, substances may be present which are liable to expand slowly under moist conditions, so causing disruption of the concrete. Clinker aggregate is not recommended for use in reinforced concrete or in concrete required to withstand severe exposure.

3.2.3   Sizes of aggregate

Most concretes contain an aggregate of 20 mm (¾ in.) maximum size graded down to particles of about 75 μm (No. 200). However, maximum sizes of 40 mm (1½ in.) and 10 mm (3/8 in.) are often used, and larger maximum sizes of up to 150 mm (6 in.) and even more have been used in mass work.

In general, more economical concretes are produced by using as large a maximum size as possible as this reduces the amount of cement required in the concrete, so lowering the cost and leading to the development of less heat of hydration (see Chapter 6.10). The limitations to size can be:
(1)   the size of the section of concrete to be cast, which should not be less than about four times the maximum aggregate size;
(2)   the concrete cover to embedded steel, which should generally be not less than the maximum size of aggregate and may have to be somewhat greater in the case of permeable aggregates (see Chapter 5.3);
(3)   some methods of designing reinforced concrete structures, which require that a relation between the bar size, bar spacing and aggregate maximum size should be observed;
(4)   the increased cost of mixing concrete and maintaining mixers where the size is about 150 mm (6 in.) and above; and
(5)   the economic availability of suitable aggregate.
The maximum sizes of synthetic lightweight aggregates will not necessarily be the same as the numerical values quoted above. This is because the process of manufacture of the aggregate may automatically lead to some other size.

Maximum sizes are typically 14 or 16 mm (½ or 5/8 in.).

An aggregate can be produced as a mixture of particles from the maximum size required down to the smallest sizes. This is generally referred to as all-in aggregate; such material is suitable for a wide range of concretes where the exact properties are not of great importance. There is, however, every likelihood that the proportion of aggregate of an intermediate size will vary widely from day to day or even from hour to hour during production and handling. The variation is due partly to variations inherent in the material or the crushing process and partly to segregation of the different sized particles during handling. For this reason it is customary in normal good-quality structural work to split aggregates into at least two parts, known as 'coarse' and 'fine' aggregate, the former being substantially larger than a 5 mm (3/16 in.) square mesh sieve size and the latter material being substantially smaller. The result is that the two sizes are batched separately; potential variation is much reduced and it becomes possible to vary the proportion of coarse and fine material to give the most satisfactory concrete. In work where a particularly high degree of control is required it is customary to split the coarse aggregate further into so-called single sizes, often of 40 to 20 mm (1½ to ¾ in.), 20 to 10 mm (¾ to 3/8 in.) and 10 to 5 mm (3/8 to 3/16 in.). A further sub-division at 14 mm (½ in.) is also used for special purposes, such as to suit particular amounts of cover to steel in relatively small precast members or to obtain a very uniform size of particle for exposed aggregate work. In laboratory work it is not unusual to divide fine aggregates into single sizes of 5 to 2.36 mm (3/16 in. to No. 7), 2.36 to 1.18 mm (Nos. 7 to 14), 1.18 mm to 600 μm (Nos. 14 to 25), 600 to 300 μm (Nos. 25 to 52), 300 to 150 μm (Nos. 52 to 100), and material smaller than 150 μm (No. 100).

In practice, a considerable amount of reconstituted aggregate is also used. In this instance the coarse and fine aggregates, having been separated by screening, are then recombined in suitable proportions for concrete work before delivery to the construction site or ready mixed concrete plant. This overcomes some of the difficulties associated with variations in grading which can be experienced with all-in aggregate, though there is still a risk that different sizes of particles may segregate during handling.

Once the maximum size of aggregate and the sizes in which it is normally obtained have been considered, the smallest sizes of particles should also be considered briefly. In uncrushed aggregates there is likely to be a small proportion of material which, on testing, passes the 75 μm (No. 200) sieve. This material is usually clay or fine silt and is generally limited to 1% by weight in coarse aggregate and 3% by weight in fine aggregate. The same 3% limit is also applied to crushed gravel sands. The proportion permitted in crushed stone fine aggregates is 15%; this higher value reflects the difference in the nature of the material passing the 75 μm (No. 200) sieve. The limit for all-in or reconstituted aggregate is related to the relative proportions of coarse and fine aggregates and their respective limits. Although it is not normally recognized in specifications, there is the fact that very fine material which adheres firmly to coarse aggregate particles is likely to have a more adverse effect on the bond obtained between the coarse aggregate particles and the cement paste than would loose fine particles which merely become mixed into the cement paste.

3.2.4   Particle shape

The particle shape of aggregate is of considerable importance in the design of a concrete mix; the classification given in BS 812 : 1967 is reproduced in Table 3.3. Examples of some shapes are given in this table and shown in Figure 3.1.

Although it is possible to measure the particle shape of aggregate, it is most unusual and probably unnecessary to specify any limiting values. This is because aggregates of more angular shape tend to produce concretes which are either harsh and difficult to work or which require a higher proportion of cement and fine aggregate in the mix. The magnitude of this effect can be shown by a comparison of the voids percentage in single-sized coarse aggregates of rounded and angular particle shape compacted in a similar manner; in one set of tests the rounded material gave a voids ratio of 34% whereas the angular material had a voids ratio of nearly 41%, indicating that a considerably greater proportion of mortar would be needed with the angular material. Consequently aggregates having a high proportion of elongated or flaky particles tend to be avoided in practice.

TABLE 3.3
Particle shape.

Classification	Description	Example
rounded	fully water-worn or completely shaped by attrition	a few gravels and some lightweight aggregates
irregular	naturally irregular, or partly shaped by attrition and having rounded edges	most gravels
angular	possessing well-defined edges formed at the intersection of roughly planar faces	most crushed materials
flaky	materials of which the thickness is small relative to the other two dimensions	laminated rocks
elongated	materials, usually angular, in which the length is considerably larger than the other two dimensions	
flaky and elongated	materials having the length considerably larger than the width, and the width considerably larger than the other two dimensions	

Flaky and elongated particles can also lead to slightly greater difficulty when handling fresh concrete, for example when pumping. Excessively flaky particles may become oriented parallel to the surface during compaction of the concrete in paving work; this may lead to a reduced resistance to frost attack unless the concrete is air-entrained (see Chapter 5.7).

In practice it is not often possible to have much choice regarding particle shape. Most gravels are irregular and contain a proportion of angular (crushed) particles, whereas very few truly rounded materials are available. Crushed rock aggregates are angular with varying proportions of flaky and elongated particles. The nature of the rock and the method of crushing affect the proportion of such particles; impact crushers tend to produce better shaped material, and large crushing ratios in other types of crusher tend to produce poorer shaped material.

3.2.5   Surface texture

The surface texture of aggregate is dependent upon the nature of the parent stone and the extent to which the surface may have been worn. Although attempts have been made to relate the surface texture of aggregate particles to the properties of the concrete made with them, no important relations have been found except perhaps that aggregates of rougher texture tend to produce concretes of greater slip resistance.

3.2.6   Impurities in aggregate [15]

Aggregates, especially gravel and sand, are liable to contain impurities which may either make the production and placing of the concrete more difficult or may result in a concrete of poor durability or appearance. The principal impurities requiring consideration in the United Kingdom are as follows.

Coal or lignite
Hard coal and anthracite are chemically inert but, mixed with gravel, they could constitute a surface blemish on decorative concretes. Anthracite tends to powder when wet and particles of soft coal could be liable to frost damage and cause 'pop-outs' on the concrete surface. A limit of 0.5% by weight of the coarse aggregate has sometimes been proposed for this reason. Some other coals can break down in the presence of alkaline solutions to form brown stains.

Chalk
Soft chalk (calcium carbonate) particles can lead to surface 'pop-outs' following attack by frost. It is, however, difficult to test for such material as any arbitrary limit on calcium carbonate would also include hard chalk, limestone and some other materials which are unlikely to be harmful. To date the best guidance on the suitability of particular sources of material is that of past experience.

(a) Rounded

(b) Irregular

(c) Angular

(d) Flaky

(e) Elongated

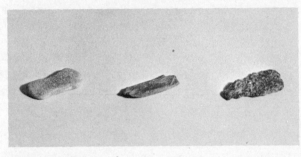

(f) Flaky and elongated

Figure 3.1 : Aggregate particle shapes.

Shell

Much aggregate is won from the sea. With it comes sea shells which can be reduced in number by good processing but which cannot be eliminated entirely. Flaky shells tend to make the concrete more harsh, and hollow shells can create voids within the concrete. In practice, any large variations in the proportion of shell from one consignment of aggregate to the next is probably more troublesome than the fact that a small proportion of shell is regularly included. Where appearance or high wearing resistance is required, a low shell content in the coarse aggregate is desirable. Shell is not generally a problem in sand, even though shell can constitute a high proportion of the material.

Sulphates

Clinker, foamed slag and air-cooled slag aggregates contain sulphate compounds; a limit of 1% sulphate (SO_3) is placed in the current British Standards for these aggregates. Despite the wide occurrence of gypsum (calcium sulphate) and some other sulphates, these do not generally contaminate natural aggregates in the United Kingdom. Gypsum, being slightly soluble, may retard the setting of cement and may, in large quantities, reduce the ultimate strength and lead to expansion and cracking of the hardened concrete. Portland cements contain a carefully controlled proportion of gypsum and, although undesirable, an aggregate with a small amount of soluble sulphate can be accepted. As a general guide, the quantity of sulphate should not be more than would double the amount of sulphate already in the cement.

Iron pyrites

Some sources of aggregates are liable too contain particles of reactive iron pyrites (ferrous sulphide) which can oxidize to form brown iron hydroxide and can cause a surface blemish. Not all forms of iron pyrites are reactive. Apart from structures where appearance is of particular importance, a very limited amount of iron pyrites can usually be tolerated.

Other sulphides

Slag aggregates can contain calcium and other sulphides in addition to small amounts of sulphates. There is a risk that some sulphides will oxidize to sulphates, bringing about attack in damp concrete. In other instances the concrete may be coloured green or blue, but sulphides are otherwise generally harmless. For these reasons, BS 1047 limits the total sulphur content to 2%.

Mica

Mica is a soft, laminated material which increases the water demand of concrete mixes. It has been shown that the strength of concrete may be reduced by 5% in the presence of 1% muscovite mica by weight of total aggregate. A limit of 1% mica has been suggested when considerations of either strength or durability indicate the need for control.

Chlorides from sea water

Aggregates, particularly those dredged from the sea, may be contaminated by sea salt which contains a high proportion of sodium chloride. The concentration is generally less than 0.1% by weight of aggregate in dredged material, even without freshwater washing. The main point to note is that the concrete should not contain more than 1.0% chloride (expressed as equivalent anhydrous calcium chloride) by weight of cement; this is a safeguard against the possibility that the chloride could lead to significant acceleration of setting in the concrete or a significant increase in the drying shrinkage of the concrete. This quantity of chloride is also not likely to have an adverse effect when used with sulphate-resisting Portland cement. On the other hand, aggregate should be virtually free of chloride when used for prestressed concrete, so as to avoid the risk of corrosion of the steel; a limit of 0.1% equivalent anhydrous calcium chloride by weight of cement would be appropriate in these circumstances.

Organic matter

Organic matter arising from active chemicals found in decaying vegetation and some other materials can retard the setting and hardening processes in concrete. Commercially available aggregates in the United Kingdom are almost always free from these impurities. In cases of doubt, comparative tests using washed and unwashed samples of the aggregate in concrete will show up any severe retardation. A laboratory test is described in BS 812.

3.2.7   Influence of aggregate on the durability of concrete

External agencies which might affect the durability of concrete, to an extent dependent on the aggregate, include the following.

Frost attack

It is relatively unusual for concrete to be damaged by frost alone (as distinct from the damage which can arise following the application of de-icing salt which accentuates frost damage very considerably). However, when it does occur, it may be associated with the use of relatively porous aggregates in an environment where the concrete is kept damp; contradictorily, very porous aggregates such as lightweight aggregates may well be less likely to be damaged because the aggregate particles never get fully saturated with water. Flaky aggregates may also aggravate possible frost damage

in paving work because the particles tend to lie parallel to the finished surface when the concrete is placed, and this may lead to later weakness (see Chapter 5.7); air-entrained concrete, which should normally be used for paving work, obviates this problem.

Attack by sulphates in ground water or soil

The subject of attack of concrete by sulphates in ground water or in soil is covered in Chapter 5. The quality of the aggregate does, however, have a minor influence on the extent of attack; porous aggregates are liable to provide an easy passage for sulphate solutions, thus accelerating attack. It is for this reason that the recommendations of Table 5.4 do not apply to lightweight aggregate concretes.

Carbonation

Concretes of high water/cement ratio, especially those which are inadequately cured, are liable to carbonate with carbon dioxide in the air. Thus aggregates containing porous particles can provide an easy passage for the carbon dioxide, so accelerating carbonation. For this reason, the concrete cover to reinforcement in lightweight aggregate concrete structures is sometimes increased by 10 mm (½ in.) as compared with dense aggregate concrete.

Aggregate properties affecting the volume change of the concrete

Concrete undergoes changes in volume when hardened; the main factors, comprising drying shrinkage, elasticity, creep and thermal expansion, are discussed in Chapter 6. In all instances, however, the type and sometimes the particular source of the aggregate will have some effect.

Alkali/aggregate reactions

The deterioration of concrete structures in some parts of the world has been attributed to reactions between the potassium and sodium hydroxides in hardened cement paste and reactive forms of silica in the aggregate. The reaction causes an expansion which cracks and disrupts the concrete. Studies have shown that the reaction is most unlikely if the alkali content of the cement, expressed as $Na_2O + 0.658 K_2O$, is below 0.6%. Since cements in the United Kingdom generally have alkali contents below this value, the problem is most unlikely to arise.

3.3   Water

Water suitable for drinking is suitable for concrete, apart from the unlikely situation of the water containing sugar. Where, however, water is obtained from the ground surface after having passed through organic materials such as peat, and is not subsequently treated, it would be advisable to test the water before using it in concrete. Water from deep boreholes is generally satisfactory without treatment, since it is most unlikely to contain organic material. BS 3148 includes requirements for the testing of water for its suitability for use in concrete. It does not give any limits with which the water should comply, although some suggestions for the interpretation of the test results are given in an appendix.

The recommended tests are based on making concrete with the suspect water, testing it, and comparing the results with otherwise similar concrete using water known from past experience to give satisfactory performance. The tests will not, however, show whether or not the concrete made with the suspect water will have adequate durability, or will display efflorescence, or will lead to accelerated rusting of embedded steel.

The alkali content of water may contribute to alkali-aggregate reaction in those aggregates containing silica in a form which reacts with sodium or potassium ions in hardened concrete to generate expansive forces sufficient to disrupt the concrete. This problem does not occur in the United Kingdom.

Sea water has been used for making concrete and has generally been satisfactory. The salt in the water may have three effects:

(1) the sodium chloride may accelerate setting and hardening in much the same way as would a deliberate addition of calcium chloride in a similar quantity;

(2) the salts may be drawn to the surface of the concrete and may show up as efflorescence when the concrete dries out;

(3) the sodium chloride may induce corrosion of reinforcement in circumstances where the concrete quality, or the cover, is inadequate. Due to the possibility of corrosion, sea water should not be used for prestressed concrete in those circumstances where the deliberate additon of calcium chloride would be prohibited.

3.4 Admixtures

3.4.1 General

Admixtures can be defined as materials other than cement, aggregate and water which are added in small quantities during mixing to produce one or more modifications to the properties of the concrete. It should not be confused with the term 'additive', which is usually reserved for an addition to cement during its production.

The number of admixture products available to the construction industry is very large and their purpose varies widely. The position is further complicated by the fact that the same admixture, used in a slightly different manner, can have slightly but significantly different effects on the properties of the concrete. It therefore becomes impossible to generalize on the advisability of using a particular admixture for particular construction work, and the subject must be approached from a basic understanding of the properties of concrete and the likely effect that particular groups of admixtures may have on those properties.[21-25] Thus the possible use of an admixture should always be based on its being beneficial and never, indiscriminately, on the assumption that it may do some good and will not do any harm.

There are three basic reasons for using admixtures:

(1) to give the concrete a particular property it does not otherwise possess;

(2) to modify some property which might otherwise hinder good concreting practice; and

(3) to reduce the cost of the concrete or the cost of placing and compacting it.

3.4.2 Water-reducing admixtures[26]

The quantity of water needed to ensure good hydration of cement is substantially less than the quantity needed to make the concrete sufficiently workable for it to be placed and compacted economically. Once the water has enabled the concrete to be fully compacted into position, the extra water needed for good workability becomes undesirable since some of it bleeds upwards, leading to weak surfaces, some forms 'water runs' up the sides of the forms, and the rest remains within the mass of the concrete, giving a water/cement ratio which governs many of the properties of the hardened concrete, including strength and durability. Consequently any means by which the total amount of water in a mix can be reduced without loss of workability is worthy of consideration.

Several groups of chemical admixtures do enable rather less water to be used in concrete without loss of workability, and of these groups some are known as 'water-reducers'. The basic forms are firstly calcium, ammonium, magnesium and sodium lignosulphonates and secondly salts of hydroxylated carboxylic acid.

The extent to which these materials enable the water content to be reduced — typically 5 to 10% — depends on many factors, including their chemical composition, the properties of the cement, the concrete mix proportions and many other variables. For example, water-reducing admixtures tend to be more effective with cements of low tricalcium aluminate and alkali content.

One of the problems associated with assessing the effectiveness of water-reducing admixtures is the measurement of concrete workability. This arises because the term 'workability' covers a number of factors which are measured to varying extents by the tests normally used. Whilst no research has been undertaken to determine which of the available methods of measuring workability is the best measure of the effectiveness of water-reducing admixtures, it seems likely that the Vebe consistometer is preferable because the test conditions are nearer to the practical situations in which concrete is placed and compacted than either the slump test alone or the compacting factor test. Practical experience using the slump test suggests that a concrete containing a water-reducing admixture may have the same slump as a plain mix and yet may prove the easier to handle and compact, since it tends to be more cohesive. This is probably due, at least in part, to the fact that the lignosulphonate type of admixture tends to entrain 1.5 to 2% of air into the mix. This entrained air, though insufficient to enable the concrete to be classed as air-entrained concrete, is not detrimental and could on occasion be of overall benefit to the properties of the hardened concrete. Some proprietary admixtures of this type contain a further ingredient to reduce the entrainment of air.

Another notable effect of the lignosulphonate type of admixture is a general tendency for the fresh concrete to bleed less. Some water-reducing admixtures based on lignosulphonate may lead to a slightly greater drying shrinkage than a plain concrete, even though the water/cement ratio may have been decreased.

The inclusion of a hydroxy-acid-type admixture in concrete has little influence on cohesiveness and may tend to increase bleeding. It does not normally lead to the entrainment of additional air.

3.4.3 Retarders

Concrete loses workability and stiffens gradually after mixing so that it can no longer be remoulded or fully compacted after a period of some hours. The length of this period varies, depending primarily on the original water/cement ratio, the workability of the concrete and the temperature. In practice it may prove expedient to extend this time so as to continue working at a relatively high temperature, or to prevent cold joints in a large mass of concrete which takes many hours to cast.

Retarding admixtures are chemically similar in many respects to water-reducing admixtures and many proprietary admixtures combine the two properties. Indeed the basic raw materials from which both types are made are the same, or so similar as to make the distinction between the two rather difficult. The chemical component leading to retardation is likely to be a cellulose or a starch.

The quantity of admixture used will depend on the extent of retardation required, which is generally between two and six hours, though periods of 24 hours or even more are possible. When using retarders, it is important to note that the effectiveness of a particular dosage is dependent on the temperature of the concrete; for example, a dosage chosen to be effective at 20°C might lead to excessive retardation if the temperature unexpectedly dropped to 10°C. Accidental overdosages have led to concrete not setting for up to ten days. One rather sophisticated use of a retarder is to gradually reduce the dosage during the casting of a large pour, taking perhaps ten hours, so that the whole mass attains a similar state of setting and hardening at the end of the pour.

When batching retarders, it is important to add the admixture at the same time in the mixing cycle because retarders added towards the end of mixing can lead to considerably greater retardation than a similar dosage at the beginning of mixing.[27, 28]

Concretes retarded for about four hours will probably attain a similar strength after 24 hours to a concrete without the admixture. The striking times for formwork are therefore not generally affected. There could, however, be an increase in formwork pressure.

3.4.4 The use of water-reducing and retarding admixtures

Since water-reducing admixtures may enable a lower water content to be used than might be necessary in an otherwise similar plain concrete, it follows that the admixture can be used in one of three ways:
(1) to reduce the water/cement ratio and so increase the strength of the concrete;
(2) to increase the workability of the concrete without increasing the water content; or
(3) to reduce both the water content and the cement content while maintaining the same water/cement ratio and workability.

If the previous discussion on the measurement of workability is kept in mind, it will be seen that these three methods of use cannot be clearly separated. But in general (1) would be used where difficulty is experienced in attaining high-strength concrete which would otherwise require a very low workability, (2) is a means of increasing the speed at which a large mass of concrete can be placed, and (3) is a means of reducing the heat of hydration and the cost of the concrete, against which has to be placed the cost of the admixture and its control. Concrete subject to excessive bleeding, due possibly to the use of an unsuitably graded aggregate or to the need to use an unusually high workability, can often benefit by the use of a water-reducing admixture. The impermeability of concrete can sometimes be improved by a reduction in the water content of the concrete. Water-reducing admixtures can, however, increase the extent of plastic cracking in freshly laid concrete.[29]

Retarding admixtures are principally of benefit in hot climates where the rapid rate of loss of workability could prove troublesome. The number of circumstances justifying the use of retarders in the United Kingdom is probably quite limited.

The use of retarders as a means of reducing the heat of hydration in mass concrete structures has been suggested, since a slow rate of chemical reaction would appear beneficial. This is, however, only of practical significance where the heat evolved is largely able to escape from the mass of the concrete before the maximum temperature is reached. This could happen in relatively small masses of concrete. In large masses, where adiabatic or nearly adiabatic conditions apply, the better way of using a chemical admixture is to use a water-reducing retarder in such a way as to reduce the cement content of the concrete by perhaps 10% compared with a plain concrete of similar strength and workability.[30]

3.4.5 Calcium chloride

Calcium chloride is one of the most widely used admixtures. It increases the rate of chemical hydration of the cement and so reduces the setting time and quickens the rate at which early strength is gained and heat of hydration is evolved. The principal applications are for cold-weather working, for repair and other urgent work, to enable early striking of formwork, to limit any deficiency brought about by little or no curing, and for working in the tidal range of the sea.

Probably the most frequent application in the United Kingdom is in cold weather when there is, for example, a night frost of −3°C followed by a day temperature of 5 to 10°C. A concrete of relatively high cement content and containing calcium chloride could be mixed to an initial temperature of about 5°C, placed and covered with insulation for perhaps three days. Thereafter frost is unlikely to have any adverse effect on the concrete other than perhaps increasing the time before props can be removed from the suspended parts of a structure. The use of calcium chloride alone, however, is not sufficiently effective to allow work to continue under freezing conditions without other precautions being taken.

When working at more normal temperatures of 15°C to 20°C and using calcium chloride in order to speed construction, it is important that the concrete should be placed rapidly, generally within half an hour of mixing. In this instance, the normal dosage of calcium chloride would lead to an increase of compressive strength of 3 to 7 N/mm² (400 to 1000 lbf/in²) at early ages. At lower temperatures, the accelerating effect of the admixture will offset the retarding effect of the low temperature so that, after three days, the admixture will have approximately the same strength at 5°C as could a concrete without the admixture at 15°C.

The maximum dosage of calcium chloride is 1.5% anhydrous by weight of cement in reinforced concrete though, when using marine aggregates, a rather lower dosage would be appropriate in order to allow for any sodium chloride already in the aggregates (see Chapter 3.3 for the effects of using sea water to mix concrete). Although calcium chloride is generally specified in the anhydrous form, it is most important that it should be in the form of a solution when added to concrete.

There are, however, several disadvantages associated with the use of calcium chloride.

(1) The drying shrinkage is increased, depending on the concentration of calcium chloride. For example, a dosage of 2% anhydrous by weight of cement would lead to an increase of about 70% at four days and about 15% after three months.

(2) Calcium chloride decreases the ability of concrete to protect embedded steel from corrosion, to an extent which depends upon the quality of the concrete and the cover to the steel. Instances of severe corrosion of embedded steel have occurred and have generally been associated with calcium chloride additions of about 3% or more anhydrous by weight of cement, or with low-quality concretes having a cover to the steel of only 10 to 15 mm (about ½ in.). Research, and experiences such as these, have led to the general recommendation to limit calcium chloride to 1.5% anhydrous by weight of cement. However, calcium chloride should never be used in prestressed concrete in such a way that it can come into contact with the prestressing tendons. Calcium chloride can also lead to corrosion of some other embedded metals including copper, aluminium and other non-ferrous metals, and

either the combination should be avoided or the metal given a protective coating.

(3) The inclusion of calcium chloride is liable to reduce the sulphate resistance of Portland cement concrete[31] so that its use is best avoided where sulphate attack is possible. It is not recommended for use with sulphate-resisting Portland cement.

(4) Whilst the acceleration of the evolution of the heat of hydration is beneficial in cold-weather work, the increase can be a disadvantage in warmer conditions and may lead to cracking of the concrete as it finally cools down. It is therefore rarely used in hot weather, except for precast work.

Although none of the above effects impose any limits on the quantity of calcium chloride which can be used in concrete not containing any embedded metal, the increases in the speed of setting, in the rate of evolution of heat of hydration and in the drying shrinkage have shown in practice that it is not generally advisable to use more than about 2% anhydrous calcium chloride.

As a result of the disadvantages associated with the use of calcium chloride, considerable efforts have been made to find an alternative with all the advantages but none of the disadvantages. Although several materials have been tried and some marketed, none yet constitute a real alternative for many applications.

3.4.6 Air entrainment

As is discussed more fully in Chapter 5.7, most concretes, after hardening for several days in temperate climates, are unlikely to suffer any significant damage during their later life as a result of frost. Examples of damage are few and can generally be traced to the use of a highly absorptive aggregate or a low-quality concrete in conditions where the concrete was virtually saturated before being rapidly frozen. The harmful effects of surface scaling brought about by freezing and thawing are, however, much increased if the hardened concrete is frozen while wet and then de-frosted by salt.

The most satisfactory remedy to possible salt damage, and often the only one, is to use air-entrained concrete. Air entrainment is brought about by including an admixture, usually a neutralized vinsol resin, during the mixing of the concrete. The mixing action then causes the formation of a very large number of semi-discrete, spherical air bubbles of diameters generally between 20 and 2000 μm (0.0008 and 0.08 in.). In order that all the concrete is protected from possible damage, the air bubbles must be not more than about 0.4 mm (0.016 in.) apart. To achieve this, the total quantity of air needed is about 13% of the cement paste or, allowing for the coarse aggregate, about 7% for a 10 mm (3/8 in.) maximum size aggregate, 5% for a 20 mm (¾ in.) maximum size and 4% for a 40 mm (1½ in.) maximum size.

One requirement of an air-entraining admixture is that, when used, it should lead to the formation of bubbles small enough to be fairly stable during the handling, placing and compacting of the concrete. Large air bubbles are less stable. The size of the air bubbles produced is, in effect, a distinction between those admixtures which may incidentally cause the inclusion of air in the mix and those described as genuine air-entraining admixtures.

The mechanism by which air entrainment protects concrete from damage by freezing and thawing is not fully understood, and several theories have been put forward. Which of the theories is correct is, however, irrelevant to most users, who need merely to note the virtually complete success of air entrainment in preventing damage.

The inclusion of entrained air would at first sight suggest that the strength of the concrete is significantly lowered; this effect is, however, not great in practice because the quantity of water required to produce a workable concrete is less than would be required in an otherwise similar plain mix. This lowering of the water/cement ratio largely, and sometimes completely, offsets the possible lowering of the strength due to deliberately entrained air.

Typically the dosage of air-entraining admixture is about 0.05% by weight of cement, though many factors will affect the actual dosage chosen, including the type, maximum size and grading of aggregate, the type and size of the mixer and the size of the batch. The inclusion of other admixtures may also affect the required dosage of an air-entraining admixture; for example, an increased dosage may be needed when also using calcium chloride or pulverized-fuel ash (see also Chapter 6.5).

Another use of air entrainment is to reduce further the density of lightweight aggregate concrete by including 20 to 30% of air in the mix. This also considerably improves its thermal insulating characteristics (see also Chapter 6.7.2).

3.4.7 Finely divided powders

Finely divided powders such as crushed rock flour, bentonite, diatomaceous earth, trass and ground granulated blastfurnace slag can on occasions be incorporated beneficially in concrete. Lean concretes of high workability can give rise to excessive bleeding which can be reduced considerably by using an appropriate admixture in the concrete, which then becomes considerably more cohesive and easier to handle.

If powders are incorporated in relatively rich concretes, the total amount of mixing water may have to be increased to make the concrete workable, with the result of lowered strength and increased drying shrinkage. In lean concretes, however, the inclusion of the admixture may well not affect the total amount of water required.

3.4.8 Pulverized-fuel ash[32]

Pulverized-fuel ash ('fly ash') of appropriate particle size and correct chemical composition, complying with BS 3892, can be incorporated in concrete in much higher quantities than are used for other types of admixture. Additions would generally be in the range 20 to 100% of the weight of cement.

The selection of an ash for use in concrete needs to be considered very carefully; particular attention should be paid to the specific surface and the loss-on-ignition of the ash. The sulphate content of the ash, expressed as SO_3, should be below 2.5% where the quantity of ash to be used is less than or equal to the quantity of cement, and below 1.5% if it exceeds it.

Some sources of pulverized-fuel ash are pozzolanas; that is, they may contribute to the strength of the concrete by combining with the free lime left after the hydration of the cement. The strength contribution takes several months to develop to a significant extent, and therefore pulverized-fuel ash is only appropriate for use in structures for which an early-age strength is of little importance. This situation arises in mass structures such as dams, where the development of the heat of hydration of the cement may lead to an excessive build-up of temperature in the concrete and subsequently to cracking on cooling. Thus a correctly designed mix incorporating pulverized-fuel ash, which itself contributes little or no heat, may be beneficial in reducing the risk of cracking. The amount of the reduction in the heat of hydration is, however, less certain.

A further effect can be brought about by using pulverized-fuel ash as a partial replacement for the fine aggregate in concrete. Pulverized-fuel ash may be appropriate for use where relatively low compressive strength is required, but such concretes are likely to have a low proportion of cement and thus to be harsh and difficult to handle, place and compact. Thus the replacement of some of the aggregate by the ash tends to increase the cohesiveness of the concrete in much the same way as some of the finely divided powders.

3.4.9 Pigments

Pigments are white or coloured fine powders which are completely insoluble in the material intended to be coloured. The requirements for satisfactory pigments in concrete are onerous as they must be light-fast and chemically resistant to both the alkalis in the concrete and the acids in industrial atmospheres. They should not adversely effect the properties of concrete, nor change colour on steam curing, nor wash out in service. Further, they should be inexpensive.

The most widely used colours are black (to produce a dark grey concrete), browns and red. The advantages of these colours are that the pigments can be based on inexpensive iron oxide or carbon black, which are both stable. Many other colours are available, though they tend to be more expensive or to be less stable. Where possible, a pigment should comply with BS 1014.

Pigments are generally sold as dry powders, though paste-like dispersions are also available. A pigment powder is generally added directly to the dry concrete mix. Suspensions can be made up shortly before needed, though they must be continually agitated until used.

Efflorescence is the main difficulty associated with the use of pigments. The movement of water from the mass of concrete to the surface during drying out can bring white salts to the surface and deposit them there, so masking the intended colour. The condition most liable to lead to efflorescence is when freshly cast concrete is exposed to cold drying winds. The addition of water-repellent admixtures or additives may alleviate the problem by reducing moisture movement through the concrete. To remove efflorescence, surfaces can be washed with dilute hydrochloric acid after hardening.

Black
Carbon black is a finely divided form of carbon with a specific surface around $58\,000$ m^2/kg and has a high tinctorial strength and good temperature resistance. On the other hand, it has a greasy surface and can be difficult to disperse in concrete, and so may be marketed with a carrier or an anionic wetting agent. According to Kroone,[33] up to 2% of carbon black by weight of cement should have no adverse effects on concrete and, although jet black concrete may not be obtained with this quantity, dark grey concretes can normally be satisfactorily obtained at lower addition rates.

Another form of carbon, known as acetylene black, can be incorporated in semi-conducting concrete flooring for use in hospital operating theatres. Synthetic black iron oxide can also be used, although it is not stable above 160°C. The tinctorial strength is lower than that of carbon black, but good grades produce permanent dark grey tints at addition rates of 2 to 4% by weight of cement.

Brown
Iron oxides are also the basis of brown pigments. Naturally occurring materials are inexpensive, though synthetic materials have a better tinctorial strength. Brown oxides change colour on heating but should be stable up to about 110°C.

Red
Red pigments can also be based on natural iron oxides. These are less expensive than synthetic materials but have a poor tinctorial strength.

Yellow
Yellow pigments based on yellow ochre are available but have a lower tinctorial strength than synthetic materials. Due to the needle-like shape of the particles, concretes may require a slightly greater amount of mixing water to obtain satisfactory workability.

Green
Chromium oxide can be used as the basis of a very stable but relatively costly pigment for concrete. Synthetic materials are therefore sometimes used.

Blue
Blue cobalt spinel is a satisfactory but extremely expensive pigment; phthalocyanine blue, an organic material, can be used as an alternative. Ultramarine is sensitive to alkalis in cement and is irreversibly bleached unless stabilized with a coating.

White
Titanium oxide, used typically at the rate of 5% by weight of cement, is sometimes used to increase the whiteness of white cement concrete.

3.4.10 Water-repellent admixtures

The structure of hardened concrete includes a continuous network of capillary pores which may or may not become blocked, depending upon the water/cement ratio of the concrete and the extent of the chemical hydration which has taken place. If the pores are continuous, water can pass through to an extent dependent upon the size and number of the pores. The surface of the concrete and the inner surface of the pores can, however, be given a water-repellent property by the inclusion of an admixture such as calcium or ammonium stearate or oleate so that water cannot so easily be absorbed into or pass through the concrete. Some admixtures used for this purpose can also cause the entrainment of relatively large bubbles of air, with the result that the permeability of the concrete to water under pressure can be increased.

Although water-repellent admixtures can reduce the passage of liquid water through concrete, they seem relatively ineffective in stopping water vapour or water under high pressure. It seems likely that the best contribution which admixtures can make towards a watertight concrete, if such a contribution is needed, is to use water-reducing admixtures in such a way as to improve the workability and cohesiveness of the concrete and so reduce the risk of poor compaction or thermal cracking in thick concrete sections.

Open-textured decorative concretes can benefit by the inclusion of water-repellent admixtures which make the concrete self-cleansing when exposed to the weather, though the effect tends to diminish with time.

3.4.11 Admixtures to aid pumping

The use of admixtures as a possible aid to pumping (see also Chapter 6.23) has been studied.[34] The results show that air-entraining admixtures, wetting agents, flocculating agents (based on cellulose ethers) and bentonite have all shown advantages, depending on the circumstances of use; these include the length of the pipeline, pump and pipeline pressures, the voids content of the coarse aggregate, the grading of the fine aggregate and the cement content. It appears that the cellulose ethers might prove most successful, but their use in structural concrete has been limited by a lack of knowledge of other effects of the admixture on the properties of the concrete.

Mix design for strength and workability

4.1 General procedure

The procedure of mix design best adopted will depend upon the particular properties of concrete specified and the particular conditions under which the concrete will be placed. In the majority of circumstances the properties specified will be the minimum or characteristic strength, the type of cement, the maximum size and type of aggregate and the minimum cement content to meet durability requirements, details of which are given in Chapter 5.

The initial stages in any mix design involve three approaches.

(1) From the specified minimum or characteristic strength the intended mean or target strength is estimated (see Chapter 4.22).

(2) From the details of the cement and aggregate specified, those sources of material available for the work are examined to assess their suitability for use (see Chapters 3.1 and 3.2). The first choice for constituent materials is clearly to use those of the lowest cost and therefore, generally, those which are closest to the site of the work. It may, however, happen that local materials prove unsuitable and other sources have to be examined; this is particularly liable to happen in the case of high-strength concretes with an average compressive strength of more than about 70 N/mm² (10 000 lbf/in²).

(3) From a knowledge of the nature of the work to be undertaken, the required workability of concrete is selected (see Chapter 4.3).

Once these data have been compiled, the selection of the mix proportions can be undertaken, though the exact procedure will depend upon the particular properties required of the concrete. The general case with Portland cement and natural aggregates is described in Chapter 4.4, which refers to concretes having an average compressive strength up to about 45 N/mm² (6500 lbf/in²). Higher compressive strengths, up to about 80 N/mm² (11 500 lbf/in²), are described in Chapter 4.5, and still higher strengths in Chapter 4.6.

Sometimes it is necessary to design not just one mix but a whole range of mixes for many purposes. This situation applies particularly to a newly established ready mixed concrete plant. A different approach is therefore described in Chapter 4.8.

Whichever of these mix design procedures is adopted, the requirements for the durability of the concrete described in Chapter 5 will have to be considered, as may one or more of the special considerations described in Chapter 6.

4.2 Strength margin

As discussed in Chapter 1, concrete varies in strength, and the intended mean or target strength required during construction work must exceed the specified minimum or characteristic strength by a margin at least sufficient to meet the variation likely to occur. This margin (sometimes called the 'current margin') is related to the anticipated standard deviation of test results and the percentage of test results permitted below the specified strength. If 5% of test results is permitted below the specified value, then the strength margin is equal to a k value of 1.64 times the anticipated standard deviation. (See Chapter 1.2, Figure 1.2 for other values of k.) There may be circumstances where a greater margin is used to facilitate more economical work (for example, in precast work where a high early strength may be required to facilitate early striking from moulds), though in this discussion the lowest reasonable margin is assumed in order that the best economy of concrete constituents should be obtained.

The accuracy with which the margin can be calculated is therefore directly dependent upon the accuracy of the standard deviation. This in turn is dependent upon the number of past results available for the purpose of calculating that standard deviation. Where less than 40 results from different batches are available, the resulting standard deviation is not likely to be accurate enough to be used, and therefore the margin adopted must be chosen to meet all likely contingencies and must therefore be large. Suitable values are given in Table 4.1.

Where between 40 and 100 test results are available from work in which the same plant and similar constituent materials have been used over a period of not less than five days but not more than six months, the margin should be 1.64 times the standard deviation. There is, however, the possibility that even 40 or more test results may indicate such a low standard deviation as cannot reasonably be expected to continue during future work. The margin should therefore be subject to an over-riding minimum, suitable values of which are given in Table 4.1.

Where over 100 test results are available from work in which the same plant and similar materials have been used over a period not exceeding twelve months, the resulting standard deviation is likely to be reasonably accurate, and the control to be exercised in the future is unlikely to differ significantly from that of the past. The margin can then be based on 1.64 times the standard deviation with the less exacting over-riding minimum given in Table 4.1.

TABLE 4.1
Minimum margin (taken from CP 110).

Number of previous test results available for determination of likely standard deviation	Characteristic compressive strength – N/mm² (lbf/in²)	Minimum margin
less than 40	less than 20 (2900)	2/3 of characteristic strength
	20 (2900) and over	15 N/mm² (2200 lbf/in²)
40 to 100	less than 20 (2900)	1/3 of characteristic strength
	20 (2900) and over	7.5 N/mm² (1100 lbf/in²)
over 100	less than 20 (2900)	1/6 of characteristic strength
	20 (2900) and over	3.75 N/mm² (550 lbf/in²)

4.3 Workability

The workability of concrete has been measured by a variety of test procedures, and it is certainly true to say that none of them, by themselves, represent accurately the ease with which the concrete can be handled, placed and compacted. This follows from the fact that the term 'workability' covers several different properties which are not only represented to different extents by the test procedures usually adopted but also take on different degrees of importance from one job to another.

One breakdown of the properties described by the general term 'workability' has been made by Newman[35] as follows:

(1) compactability, or the ease with which concrete can be compacted and air voids removed;

(2) mobility, or the ease with which concrete can flow into moulds, around steel and be remoulded; and

(3) stability, or ability of the concrete to remain a stable coherent, homogeneous mass during handling and vibration without the constituents segregating.

As a result of these and other considerations, it is convenient to ascribe designations of 'high', 'medium', 'low', 'very low' and 'extremely low' to particular degrees of workability and to relate these to the test procedures most generally adopted and to the conditions of placing the concrete. Details are given in Table 4.2. In reading this table it is important to realize that if the workability of a particular concrete mix were measured by each of the test procedures — slump, compacting factor and Vebe — the results might well not coincide with all the values quoted; this is because some properties of the concrete, for example the particle shape of the coarse aggregate, might have a greater influence on one test procedure than on another.

A typical relation between the different test procedures is shown in Figure 4.1.[36] The data apply to 20mm (¾ in.) maximum-size gravel and crushed rock coarse aggregate with natural sand used in mixes with aggregate/cement ratios from 3 to 9 by weight. With crushed rock fine aggregate the same relation between slump and Vebe time is obtained, though the values of compacting factor tend to be low in relation to either of the other test procedures. A further point to note is that values refer to concretes of normal density, about 2400 kg/m³ (150 lb/ft³), and that rather different values prove preferable for lightweight concretes (see Chapter 6.7.2). The numerical values of

TABLE 4.2
Workability for different purposes and appropriate test values.

Degree of workability	Placing conditions	Nominal maximum size of aggregate – mm (in.)	Compacting factor	Slump – mm (in.)	Vebe time – s
extremely low	sections subject to extremely intensive or prolonged vibration; pressure may be also be required	10 (3/8) 20 (¾)	0.65 0.68	0 0	over 20
very low	small sections subjected to intensive vibration and large sections to normal vibration	10 (3/8) 20 (¾) 40 (1½)	0.75 0.78 0.78	0 0-10 (0-½) 0-25 (0-1)	7-20
low	simply reinforced sections with vibration and large sections without vibration	10 (3/8) 20 (¾) 40 (1½)	0.83 0.85 0.85	0-5 (0-¼) 10-25 (½-1) 25-50 (1-2)	5-10
medium	simply reinforced sections without vibration and heavily reinforced sections with vibration	10 (3/8) 20 (¾) 40 (1½)	0.90 0.92 0.92	5-25 (¼-1) 25-50 (1-2) 50-100 (2-4)	3-5
high	heavily reinforced sections without vibration	10 (3/8) 20 (¾) 40 (1½)	0.95 0.95 0.95	25-100 (1-4) 50-125 (2-5) 100-175 (4-7)	2-3

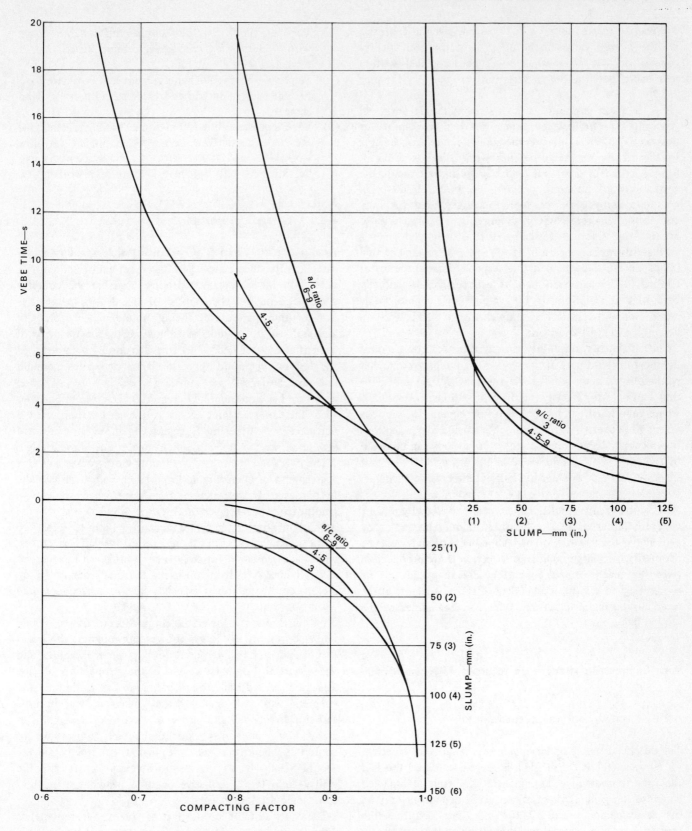

Figure 4.1 : Some relations between workability tests, indicating the effect of the aggregate/cement ratio by weight.

compacting factor, slump and Vebe time given in Table 4.2 are the *average* values to be used; for purposes of quality control on site, the values must be associated with a reasonable batch-to-batch variation, as given in Chapter 1.4.2.

For a given strength, the lowest materials cost will generally be obtained by using as low a workability as possible. The cost of placing the concrete, however, is liable to be greatly increased as the workability is reduced. Further, there is a general tendency to under-estimate the workability of concrete needed, which can lead to incomplete compaction on site. Since the need for fully compacted concrete is vitally important, it is preferable to err on the side of designing for a little too high a workability rather than a little too low. The making of trial mixes can be deceptive in this respect, because the effort applied to the compaction of a test specimen is generally very high in relation to the volume of concrete being compacted and certainly very much higher than is likely to be applied in most site work.

The choice of workability should also take into account the most difficult part of the work to be undertaken; higher workability is required for the bottom layer in a lift, for thin sections, for heavily reinforced sections, for sections where reinforcement bars cross or are lapped, for sections where the cover to reinforcement is small and for sections of awkward shape. Some of these conditions can be eased by reducing the maximum size of the aggregate below that specified, though this has the indirect effect of requiring an increase in the cement content of the concrete.

Difficult placing conditions can often be eased by placing concrete rather more slowly or in thinner layers, or by prolonging the vibration; These expedients often have to be adopted where large quantities of concrete are produced at once (eg ready mixed concrete), and it would not be economical to set the workability of all the concrete at the level appropriate for perhaps one awkward corner of the section being cast.

4.4 Compressive strength up to about 45 N/mm² (6500 lbf/in²

4.4.1 Strength and water/cement ratio

The design of mixes to have average strengths up to about 45 N/mm² (6500 lbf/in²)[1] is greatly eased by the fact that the compressive strength of the fully compacted concrete can generally be assumed to be dependent only on the water/cement ratio of the mix, provided that the properties of the cement and the curing conditions remain the same. Thus the average water/cement ratio can be determined directly from the target mean strength, using Figure 4.2, for Portland cement complying with BS 12. This graph has been compiled from the relation between water/cement ratio and 28-day strength used to arrive at the mix proportions for prescribed mixes (Table 2.3), and from other data[71] to arrive at the strengths at other ages. In using Figure 4.2 several important points should be noted.

(1) The data apply to fully compacted concrete made with natural dense aggregate and cured at a temperature of about 15°C.
(2) Sulphate-resisting Portland cement and Portland blast-furnace cement should be treated as ordinary Portland cement.
(3) Experience has shown that somewhat higher strengths may be expected with concretes of low and very low workability and, conversely, that lower strengths may be expected with concretes of very high workability.

4.4.2 Aggregate properties

As discussed in Chapter 3.2.4, the particle shape of aggregate affects the quantity of cement-and-water mortar needed in the concrete to produce a stable and cohesive concrete. Thus, for the purpose of mix design, the description of the aggregate as being 'rounded', 'irregular' or 'angular' can be used to assist in judging the quantity of cement and water needed in a mix. It should be noted that the description should apply to all the aggregates used and not just the largest particle size; since, however, the fine aggregate has a considerably greater surface area of particles than the coarse aggregate, it is the description of the particle shape of the fine aggregate which predominates and should be used in the subsequent operations of mix design.

The overall or combined grading of both coarse and fine aggregate is of considerable importance with regard to the properties of fresh concrete. For convenience, some type grading curves are given in Figures 4.3, 4.4 and 4.5 for nominal maximum aggregate sizes of 10 mm (3/8 in.), 20 mm (¾ in.) and 40 mm (1½ in.) respectively. These curves, which are numbered for convenience, must not be regarded as being ideal or as being preferred to other gradings — they are merely the gradings which relate to subsequent data given, for example, in Tables 4.3 to 4.11.

Within limits, the lower the proportion of fine aggregate in the concrete (the lower the grading number) the lower the cement content required for a given workability and water/cement ratio. However, if the proportion of fine aggregate is reduced too far below the optimum, the concrete will lack stability and cohesion, will become difficult to handle and liable to excessive bleeding after compaction, and may indeed become impossible to compact. Therefore, the proportion of fine aggregate should ideally be as low as possible consistent with the ability to obtain a cohesive concrete which can be fully compacted economically.

The most suitable proportion of fine aggregate depends upon many factors. The more important ones can be listed as follows.
(1) The finer the grading of the fine aggregate, the lower the proportion, expressed as a percentage of the total aggregate, needed to produce a concrete of otherwise similar properties. Conversely, the coarser the grading of fine aggregate, the more will be needed.
(2) The smaller the maximum size of the coarse aggregate, the greater the proportion of fine aggregate needed for concretes of similar cement content and workability.

(3) The lower the cement content of the mix, the greater the optimum proportion of fine aggregate needed.

(4) The more angular the particle shape of the coarse aggregate, the greater the proportion of fine aggregate needed.

(5) The smaller the section to be cast and the more congested it is with reinforcement and cable ducts, the greater the proportion of fine aggregate needed.

(6) The higher the workability of the concrete, the greater the proportion of fine aggregate needed.

(7) The proportion of fine aggregate should be increased where the concrete is more liable to segregate during handling or placing — for example, concrete being placed by a chute or a pump.

(8) The proportion may have to be increased for concrete which is to be placed in a situation where loss of mortar is possible — for example, when placed underwater or in formwork which is not mortar-tight.

(9) The proportion of fine aggregate may have to be increased or decreased for concrete whose appearance is of prime importance (see Chapter 6.3).

Consideration of several of these factors shows them to derive quite simply from some of the more complex mix design procedures mentioned in Chapter 1.

Specific surface of aggregate

Some mix design procedures are dependent upon the fact that the total surface area of all the aggregate particles is directly related to the amount of water needed in concrete to produce a certain workability.[3] Now, the specific surface of a given weight of aggregate increases as the particle size decreases; assuming the aggregates to be of a similar particle shape, the specific surface doubles as the particle size is halved. The surface area of particles also increases as the particle shape changes from rounded to irregular, to angular, to flaky and to elongated. Point (1) above derives directly from these considerations, as does the method of combining aggregate gradings described in Chapter 7.2.3.

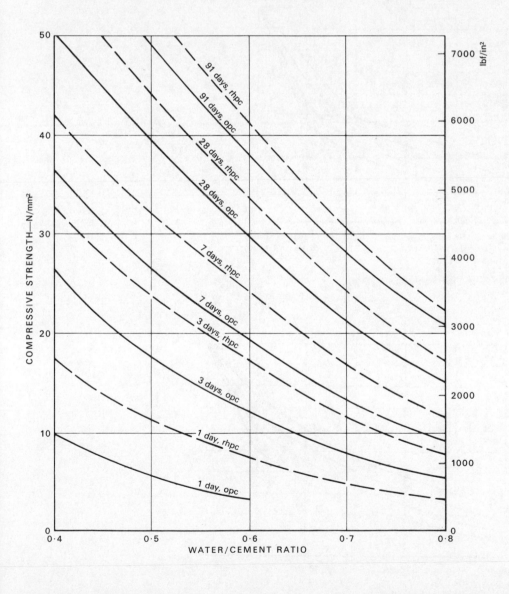

Figure 4.2 : Typical relation between compressive strength and water/cement ration for fully compacted dense aggregate concrete made with Portland cement to BS 12.

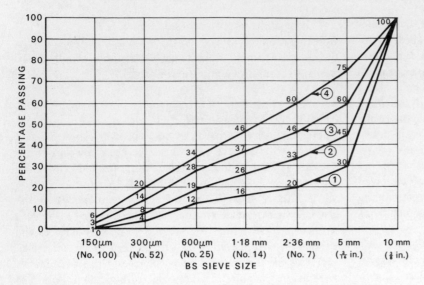

Figure 4.3 : Grading curves for 10 mm (3/8 in.) maximum-size aggregate.

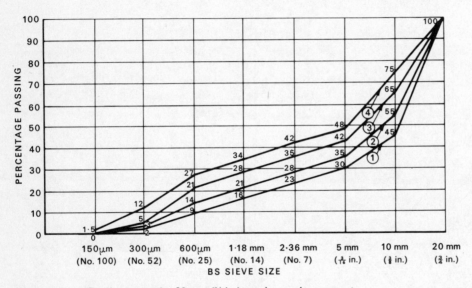

Figure 4.4 : Grading curves for 20 mm (¾ in.) maximum-size aggregate.

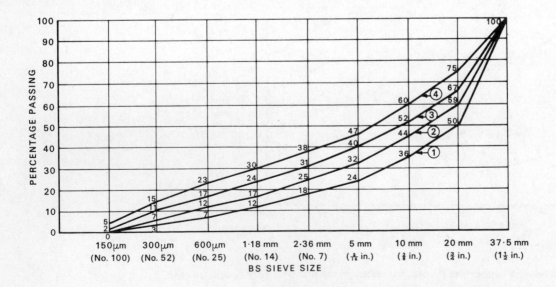

Figure 4.5 : Grading curves for 40 mm (1½ in.) maximum-size aggregate.

Voids in bulk coarse aggregate

Some methods of mix design[5] involve the use of an aggregate with a gap grading and stem from a consideration of the extent and size of voids within a mass of coarse aggregate particles. The amounts of fine aggregate, cement and water required to fill these voids is then determined in such a way as to use as low a cement content as is reasonable. Now, the greater the range of particle size over which the coarse aggregate is graded, the lower is the proportion of voids − point (4) above. The proportion of fine aggregate needed − point (2) above. Also, the more angular the aggregate particle shape, the greater is the proportion of voids − point (4) above. The proportion of voids is also increased when the natural packing of the aggregate particles is interrupted by the existence of some other material, such as forms and reinforcement − point (5) above.

4.4.3   Proportion of cement

The proportion of cement, expressed as the aggregate/cement ratio by weight, can be determined directly from Tables 4.3 to 4.11 once the type and maximum size of the aggregate available for use (Chapter 3.2.3), the required workability (Chapter 4.3) and the required water/cement ratio (Chapter 4.4.1) have been decided, and the overall aggregate grading (Chapter 4.4.2) has been considered.

In any of these tables it will be seen that, for any given workability and water/cement ratio, there is a choice of aggregate/cement ratios for different overall aggregate gradings. From the point of view of obtaining the most economical concrete, the highest aggregate/cement ratio should be selected, though the use of a relatively fine overall aggregate grading (higher grading number) may produce a concrete of better handling characteristics. The best result is often obtained by using the highest aggregate/cement ratio, except where a higher grading number is possible with an aggregate/cement ratio of perhaps 0.1 or 0.2 lower, as this ensures a reasonably cohesive concrete. There is a further point which is worth considering at this stage: due to the likely variations in aggregate grading from one consignment to another and in the accuracy of batching, it is advisable to aim for a slightly higher proportion of fine aggregate than is strictly necessary, say 5% of the total grading, because the adverse effects of using too little fine aggregate, leading possibly to segregation in handling or inadequate compaction of the concrete, are likely to be more serious than those attributable to using a little more fine aggregate than is strictly necessary.

Once the type grading and aggregate cement ratio have been estimated from one of the tables 4.3 to 4.11, it is possible to continue with the mix design by determining the combined grading of the coarse and fine aggregates and proceeding with trial mixes, as explained in Chapter 7. If this combined grading results in the omission of some of the middle sizes of aggregate (ie, a gap grading), this will have relatively little effect on the overall mix design, except possibly where the concrete is to be pumped or to have the coarse aggregate exposed.

4.4.4   Summary and example

Figure 4.6 summarizes the general procedure of selecting mix proportions for concrete made with dense aggregates and required to have an average compressive strength below 45 N/mm^2 (6500 lbf/in^2) at 28 days.

Although this section is concerned with the design of a mix to meet the requirements of strength and workability, it is also necessary to check that the concrete has an adequate durability; this is discussed in detail in Chapter 5, but it is now worth noting that the mix must meet the cement content and/or the water/cement ratios given in Table 5.2 or 5.3. Thus, in Figure 4.6, the need for meeting the durability requirements is indicated; should the design indicate that these requirements will not be met, the appropriate change should be made and cross-checked with the other factors.

Example for a typical reinforced concrete job

Specification requirements
Characteristic strength 25 N/mm^2 (3600 lbf/in^2) at 28 days
Ordinary Portland cement to BS 12
Nominal maximum size of aggregate 20 mm (¾ in.)
Aggregate to BS 882
Minimum cement content 360 kg/m^3 (605 lb/yd^3)
(taken from Table 5.2 for severe exposure − see Chapter 5 for explanation)

Data available to concrete producer
Cement available assumed to provide strengths similar to those shown in Figure 4.2
Aggregates available are an irregular gravel and a natural sand
No previous experience which would assist in fixing the strength margin lower than the 15 N/mm^2 (2200 lbf/in^2) given in Table 4.1
Workability required is 'high', from Table 4.2

Calculations
Target mean strength = 25 + 15 N/mm^2 = 40 N/mm^2 (5800 lbf/in^2)
Target mean water/cement ratio, from Figure 4.2, = 0.50
Aggregate/cement ratio from Table 4.7, using grading number 3, is 4.4 by weight

Using Figure 2.1, and assuming an aggregate specific gravity of 2.6, the cement content for the above proportions can be determined as 400 kg/m^3 (675 lb/yd^3), which meets the durability requirement.

This example is continued in Chapter 7.2.1, where the aggregate grading is further considered.

TABLE 4.3

Aggregate/cement ratios required to give four degrees of workability with different water/cement ratios and gradings.

10 mm (3/8 in.) rounded gravel aggregate

Degree of workability (Table 4.2)		Aggregate/cement ratio by weight															
		'Very low'				'Low'				'Medium'				'High'			
Grading number (Figure 4.3)		1	2	3	4	1	2	3	4	1	2	3	4	1	2	3	4
Water/cement ratio by weight	0.40	5.6	5.0	4.2	3.2	4.5	3.9	3.3	2.6	3.9	3.5	3.0	2.4	3.5	3.2	2.8	2.3
	0.45	7.2	6.4	5.3	4.1	5.5	4.9	4.1	3.2	4.7	4.3	3.7	3.0	4.2	3.9	3.4	2.9
	0.50		7.8	6.4	4.9	6.5	5.8	4.9	3.8	5.4	5.0	4.3	3.5	4.8	4.5	4.0	3.4
	0.55			7.5	5.7	7.4	6.7	5.7	4.4	6.1	5.7	4.9	4.0	5.3	5.1	4.5	3.9
	0.60				6.5		7.5	6.4	5.0	6.7	6.3	5.5	4.5	5.8	5.6	5.0	4.3
	0.65				7.2			7.1	5.6	7.3	6.9	6.1	5.0	S	6.1	5.5	4.7
	0.70							7.7	6.2	7.9	7.5	6.7	5.5		6.6	6.0	5.1
	0.75								6.7			7.2	5.9		7.1	6.5	5.5
	0.80								7.2			7.7	6.3		7.6	6.9	5.9

S indicates that the mix would segregate.

TABLE 4.4

Aggregate/cement ratios required to give four degrees of workability with different water/cement ratios and gradings.

10 mm (3/8 in.) irregular gravel aggregate

Degree of workability (Table 4.2)		Aggregate/cement ratio by weight															
		'Very low'				'Low'				'Medium'				'High'			
Grading number (Figure 4.3)		1	2	3	4	1	2	3	4	1	2	3	4	1	2	3	4
Water/cement ratio by weight	0.40	4.1	3.8	3.3	2.8	3.3	3.1	2.8	2.3								
	0.45	5.1	4.8	4.3	3.6	4.1	3.9	3.5	3.0	3.5	3.4	3.2	2.8	3.2	3.1	3.0	2.7
	0.50	6.1	5.8	5.2	4.4	4.8	4.6	4.2	3.7	4.2	4.1	3.8	3.4	S	3.8	3.6	3.2
	0.55	7.0	6.7	6.1	5.2	5.5	5.3	4.9	4.3	S	4.7	4.4	4.0		4.4	4.2	3.7
	0.60	7.9	7.6	7.0	6.0	S	6.0	5.6	4.9		5.3	5.0	4.5		4.9	4.7	4.2
	0.65			7.8	6.8		6.6	6.2	5.5		5.9	5.6	5.0		5.4	5.2	4.6
	0.70						7.2	6.8	6.1		6.4	6.1	5.5		5.9	5.7	5.0
	0.75						7.8	7.4	6.7		6.9	6.6	6.0		6.4	6.1	5.4
	0.80							8.0	7.3		7.4	7.1	6.4		6.8	6.5	5.8

S indicates that the mix would segregate.

TABLE 4.5

Aggregate/cement ratios required to give four degrees of workability with different water/cement ratios and gradings.

10 mm (3/8 in.) crushed rock aggregate

Degree of workability (Table 4.2)		Aggregate/cement ratio by weight															
		'Very low'				'Low'				'Medium'				'High'			
Grading number (Figure 4.3)		1	2	3	4	1	2	3	4	1	2	3	4	1	2	3	4
Water/cement ratio by weight	0.40	3.7	3.3	2.8	2.0												
	0.45	4.5	4.1	3.5	2.6	3.8	3.6	3.0	2.2	3.3	3.1	2.7	2.1				
	0.50	5.2	4.9	4.2	3.2	4.4	4.2	3.6	2.7	3.8	3.7	3.2	2.6	S	3.2	2.9	2.4
	0.55	5.9	5.6	4.9	3.8	4.9	4.8	4.2	3.2	S	4.2	3.7	3.0		3.7	3.4	2.8
	0.60	6.6	6.3	5.5	4.3	S	5.3	4.7	3.7		4.7	4.2	3.4		4.2	3.8	3.2
	0.65	7.3	7.0	6.1	4.8		5.8	5.2	4.2		5.1	4.6	3.8		4.6	4.2	3.6
	0.70	7.9	7.6	6.7	5.3		6.3	5.7	4.6		5.6	5.1	4.2		5.0	4.6	4.0
	0.75			7.3	5.8		6.8	6.2	5.0		6.0	5.5	4.6		5.4	5.0	4.4
	0.80			7.8	6.3		7.2	6.6	5.5		6.4	5.9	5.0		5.8	5.4	4.7

* With crushed aggregate of poorer shape than that tested, segregation may occur at a lower aggregate/cement ratio.

S indicates that the mix would segregate.

TABLE 4.6
Aggregate/cement ratios required to give four degrees of workability with different water/cement ratios and gradings.

20 mm (¾ in.) rounded gravel aggregate

		Aggregate/cement ratio by weight															
Degree of workability (Table 4.2)		'Very low'				'Low'				'Medium'				'High'			
Grading number (Figure 4.4)		1	2	3	4	1	2	3	4	1	2	3	4	1	2	3	4
Water/cement	0.35	4.5	4.2	3.7	3.2	3.8	3.6	3.3	3.0	3.1	3.0	2.8	2.6				
ratio by weight	0.40	6.6	6.1	5.4	4.5	5.3	5.1	4.6	4.1	4.2	4.2	3.9	3.6	3.7	3.8	3.6	3.3
	0.45	8.1	7.6	6.7	5.8	6.9	6.6	5.9	5.1	5.3	5.3	5.0	4.6	4.6	4.8	4.5	4.1
	0.50			8.0	7.0	8.2	8.0	7.0	6.0	6.3	6.3	6.0	5.5	5.5	5.7	5.4	4.8
	0.55				8.1			8.2	6.9	7.3	7.3	7.0	6.3	6.3	6.5	6.1	5.5
	0.60								7.7			8.0	7.1	S	7.2	6.8	6.1
	0.65								8.4				7.8		7.7	7.4	6.6
	0.70															7.9	7.1
	0.75																7.6

S indicates that the mix would segregate.

TABLE 4.7
Aggregate/cement ratios required to give four degrees of workability with different water/cement ratios and gradings.

20 mm (¾ in.) irregular gravel aggregate

		Aggregate/cement ratio by weight															
Degree of workability (Table 4.2)		'Very low'				'Low'				'Medium'				'High'			
Grading number (Figure 4.4)		1	2	3	4	1	2	3	4	1	2	3	4	1	2	3	4
Water/cement	0.35	3.6	3.6	3.5	3.0	3.0	3.0	3.0	2.7								
ratio by weight	0.40	4.9	4.8	4.6	4.1	3.9	3.9	3.9	3.5	3.3	3.4	3.4	3.2	3.1	3.2	3.2	2.9
	0.45	6.0	5.8	5.5	5.0	4.8	4.8	4.7	4.3	4.0	4.1	4.1	3.9	S	3.8	3.8	3.5
	0.50	7.2	6.8	6.4	5.9	5.5	5.5	5.4	5.0	4.6	4.8	4.8	4.5		4.4	4.4	4.1
	0.55	8.3	7.8	7.3	6.7	6.2	6.2	6.1	5.7	S	5.4	5.3	5.1		4.9	4.9	4.7
	0.60	9.4	8.7	8.1	7.4	6.9	6.9	6.7	6.3		6.0	5.9	5.6		S	5.4	5.2
	0.65				8.0	7.5	7.5	7.3	6.8		S	6.4	6.1			5.8	5.7
	0.70					8.0	8.0	7.8	7.3			6.8	6.6			6.2	6.1
	0.75								7.9			7.2	7.0			6.6	6.5
	0.80											7.5	7.4			S	7.0

S indicates that the mix would segregate.

TABLE 4.8
Aggregate/cement ratios required to give four degrees of workability with different water/cement ratios and gradings.

20 mm (¾ in.) crushed rock aggregate

		Aggregate/cement ratio by weight															
Degree of workability (Table 4.2)		'Very low'				'Low'				'Medium'				'High'			
Grading number (Figure 4.4)		1	2	3	4	1	2	3	4	1	2	3	4	1	2	3	4
Water/cement	0.40	4.5	4.1	3.8	3.5	3.5	3.5	3.2	3.0								
ratio by weight	0.45	5.5	5.0	4.6	4.3	4.3	4.2	3.9	3.7	3.7	3.7	3.4	3.3	3.5	3.5	3.2	3.1
	0.50	6.5	5.9	5.4	5.0	5.0	4.9	4.5	4.3	4.2	4.2	3.9	3.8	S	3.9	3.8	3.5
	0.55	7.2	6.6	6.0	5.7	5.7	5.5	5.0	4.8	4.7	4.7	4.5	4.3		S	4.3	4.0
	0.60	7.8	7.2	6.6	6.3	6.3	6.0	5.6	5.3	S	5.2	4.9	4.8			4.7	4.5
	0.65	8.3	7.7	7.2	6.9	6.9	6.5	6.1	5.8		5.7	5.4	5.2			5.2	4.9
	0.70	8.7	8.2	7.7	7.5	7.4	7.0	6.6	6.3		6.2	5.8	5.7			5.5	5.3
	0.75			8.2	8.0	7.9	7.5	7.0	6.7		S	6.2	6.1			5.8	5.7
	0.80							7.4	7.2			6.6	6.5			6.1	6.0

S indicates that the mix would segregate.

TABLE 4.9
Aggregate/cement ratios required to give four degrees of workability with different water/cement ratios and gradings.
40 mm (1½ in.) rounded gravel aggregate

Degree of workability (Table 4.2)	Aggregate/cement ratio by weight															
	'Very low'				'Low'				'Medium'				'High'			
Grading number (Figure 4.5)	1	2	3	4	1	2	3	4	1	2	3	4	1	2	3	4
Water/cement ratio by weight 0.35	5.0	4.5	3.9	3.4	4.3	3.9	3.5	3.1	3.4	3.1	2.9	2.7				
0.40	7.0	6.5	5.7	4.9	5.9	5.6	5.0	4.4	4.7	4.6	4.3	3.8	4.1	4.0	3.9	3.5
0.45	8.9	8.6	7.7	6.5	7.6	7.4	6.7	5.8	6.0	6.1	5.7	5.0	5.2	5.3	5.0	4.6
0.50				8.0			8.2	7.2	7.5	7.6	7.1	6.3	6.3	6.5	6.2	5.7
0.55								8.4		8.9	8.1	7.3	S	7.7	7.4	6.7
0.60																7.6

S indicates that the mix would segregate.

Note: These values have been obtained by extrapolation of other data and are not based directly on the results of trial mixes.

TABLE 4.10
Aggregate/cement ratios required to give four degrees of workability with different water/cement ratios and gradings.
40 mm (1½ in.) irregular gravel aggregate

Degree of workability (Table 4.2)	Aggregate/cement ratio by weight															
	'Very low'				'Low'				'Medium'				'High'			
Grading number (Figure 4.5)	1	2	3	4	1	2	3	4	1	2	3	4	1	2	3	4
Water/cement ratio by weight 0.35	4.0	3.9	3.6	3.2	3.4	3.3	3.2	2.9								
0.40	5.3	5.2	4.8	4.3	4.5	4.5	4.2	3.8	3.8	3.8	3.7	3.4	3.4	3.5	3.3	3.1
0.45	6.6	6.5	6.0	5.3	5.6	5.6	5.3	4.8	4.6	4.7	4.6	4.3	4.1	4.4	4.3	4.0
0.50	7.8	7.7	7.1	6.3	6.6	6.6	6.3	5.7	5.5	5.7	5.5	5.1	4.8	5.2	5.1	4.8
0.55			8.1	7.3	7.6	7.6	7.2	6.6	6.2	6.5	6.3	5.9	S	5.9	5.9	5.5
0.60								7.4	7.0	7.3	7.1	6.6		S	6.7	6.3
0.65								8.1	7.8	8.1	7.8	7.3			7.3	6.9
0.70												7.9				7.4
0.75																8.0

S indicates that the mix would segregate.

TABLE 4.11
Aggregate/cement ratios required to give four degrees of workability with different water/cement ratios and gradings.
40 mm (1½ in.) crushed rock aggregate

Degree of workability (Table 4.2)	Aggregate/cement ratio by weight															
	'Very low'				'Low'				'Medium'				'High'			
Grading number (Figure 4.5)	1	2	3	4	1	2	3	4	1	2	3	4	1	2	3	4
Water/cement ratio by weight 0.35	3.4	3.4	3.2	2.9												
0.40	4.9	4.6	4.2	3.8	4.0	3.8	3.6	3.3	3.3	3.3	3.2	3.0	3.1	3.1	2.9	2.7
0.45	6.0	5.7	5.2	4.7	4.9	4.7	4.4	4.2	4.1	4.1	3.9	3.8	3.7	3.8	3.7	3.4
0.50	7.2	6.8	6.2	5.6	5.8	5.6	5.3	5.0	4.8	4.8	4.7	4.6	4.4	4.5	4.5	4.2
0.55	8.1	7.7	7.1	6.4	6.6	6.4	6.1	5.8	5.5	5.5	5.4	5.3	S	5.2	5.2	4.8
0.60		8.6	8.0	7.2	7.4	7.2	6.9	6.6	6.1	6.2	6.1	6.0		S	5.9	5.6
0.65			8.8	7.9	8.1	7.9	7.6	7.3	S	6.9	6.8	6.6			6.5	6.2
0.70				8.6		8.5	8.3	7.9		7.5	7.5	7.3			7.1	6.8
0.75								8.5			8.1	7.8				7.4

S indicates that the mix would segregate.

Note: These values have been obtained by extrapolation of other data and are not based directly on the results of trial mixes.

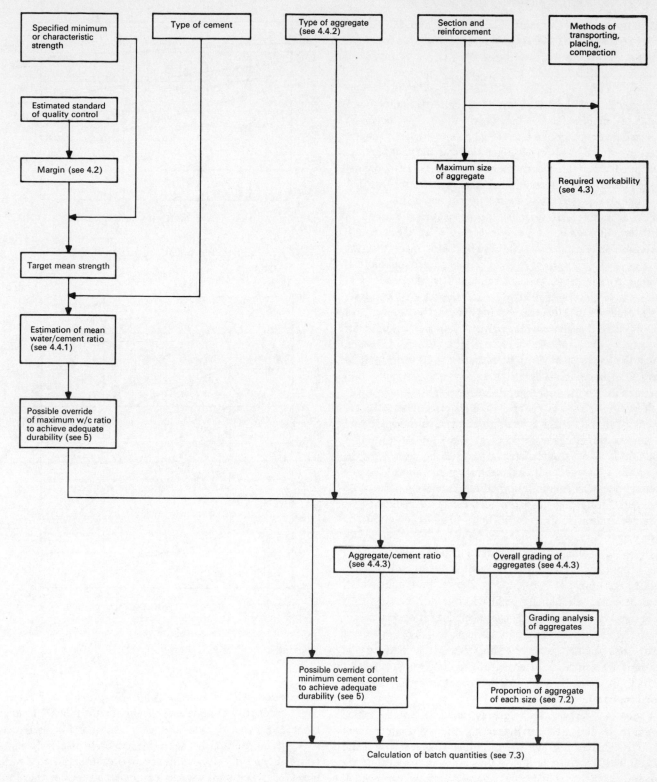

Figure 4.6 : Outline of procedure for the selection of mix proportions for concrete made with dense aggregate and required to have a target mean strength below 45 N/mm² (6500 lbf/in².) at 28 days.

4.5 Compressive strength between 45 and 80 N/mm² (6500 and 11 500 lbf/in²)

4.5.1 Principles

With the gradual improvement in concrete technology and concrete practice over the years there has been an increasing use of concretes of higher and higher strength. The advent of prestressed concrete, and particularly pre-tensioned concrete, led to the publication in 1954 of mix design data for concretes of high compressive strength,[37] though nowadays these strengths are not unusual.

For a number of reasons, the procedure described in Chapter 4.4 tends to be less accurate as the strength increases. In Chapter 4.4 the assumption is made that the compressive strength of the fully compacted concrete is related to the water/cement ratio and is independent of both the aggregate/cement ratio and the type of aggregate used. Neither of these assumptions is strictly true but, for all practical purposes, the effect can be ignored for concretes of relatively low strength. When, however, strengths in excess of about 45 N/mm² (6500 lbf/in²) at 28 days are being considered it is advisable to take into account the approximate nature of these assumptions.

For any given set of materials and water/cement ratio, the strength of the concrete tends to increase as the aggregate/cement ratio increases, that is as the cement content is decreased. The extent of the effect can be shown by the fact that a change in the aggregate/cement ratio of 0.5 at a constant water/cement ratio will have a similar effect to a change in water/cement ratio of 0.01 at a constant aggregate/cement ratio. Changes in these proportions naturally give rise to a change in the workability of the concrete. An attempt to increase the strength of concrete by adjusting the proportions of aggregate, cement and water while maintaining a constant workability shows that the water/cement ratio should be reduced; but to do this it is necessary to reduce the aggregate/cement ratio; this in turn tends to reduce the strength, though to a smaller extent than the original increase. Thus there is a limit to the amount by which the strength of the concrete at constant workability can be increased by merely altering the proportions of the constituents.

Figure 4.7 shows the relatively small extent to which strength is increased by decreasing the aggregate/cement ratio, particularly at low workabilities. However, the figure also shows that a reduction in the compacting factor of the concrete will, provided the concrete is fully compacted, increase the strength to a considerable extent. The well-proven need to use concretes of low workability compacted by vibration is clearly illustrated; for example, with reference to the materials and age of test used for the data from which Figure 4.7 was compiled, it is clearly necessary to use a mix having a compacting factor below about 0.7 in order to exceed a strength of about 50 N/mm² (7250 lbf/in²); a mix with a very high cement content and of high workability would not have been satisfactory.

The effect of the type of coarse aggregate on the compressive strength of concrete made with it is shown in Figure 4.8. Both the aggregates considered are used in

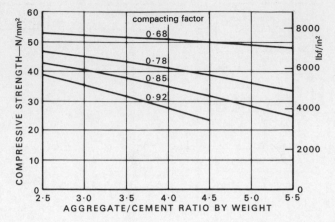

Figure 4.7 : Typical relation between compressive strength and aggregate/cement ratio for various compacting factors.

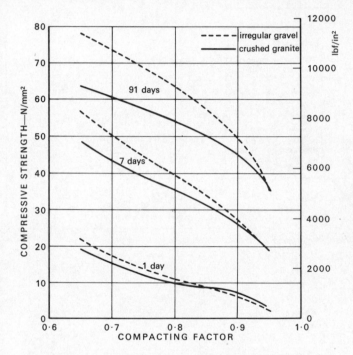

Figure 4.8 : Typical relation between compressive strength and compacting factor for two types of coarse aggregate.

conjunction with a natural sand. To provide a practical comparison, the compressive strengths are plotted against compacting factor, and the very considerably increased strength of the granite aggregate concrete is clearly illustrated. Figure 4.9 shows this comparison to apply to a wide range of types and sources of coarse aggregate; the data apply to mixes with an aggregate/cement ratio of 2.5 by weight and a compacting factor of 0.8. The dotted and chain-dotted lines refer to the mix design data given in Chapter 4.5.2 and show the aggregates used to be typical of their type. The data also show there is a ceiling value of compressive strength which is unlikely to be exceeded by the particular aggregate. For the gravel aggregates it is typically about 70 N/mm² (10 000 lbf/in²), and for the crushed rocks it is somewhat higher.

The principles underlying the design of mixes having compressive strength over about 45 N/mm² (6500 lbf/in²) which have just been discussed show that, because the

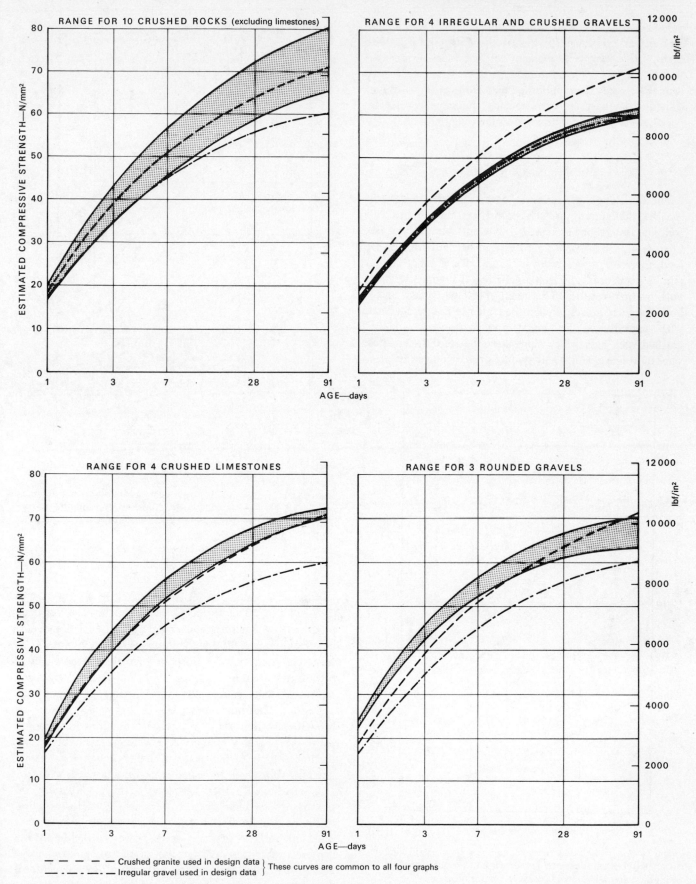

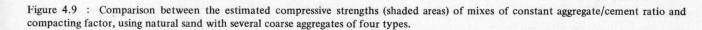

Figure 4.9 : Comparison between the estimated compressive strengths (shaded areas) of mixes of constant aggregate/cement ratio and compacting factor, using natural sand with several coarse aggregates of four types.

properties of the constituent materials have a very significant effect on the properties of the concrete made with them, an accurate assessment of the mix proportions needed to meet the requirements of a job specification cannot be made from published data alone. Additional data gained from past experience using the same constituent materials, or from trial mixes, become essential.

4.5.2 Design procedure

As in the design of mixes in other strength ranges, the specified minimum or characteristic strength of the concrete must be increased by a suitable margin (see Chapter 4.2) to arrive at a target mean strength. This is then used to arrive at an arbitrary 'reference number'. These numbers are used in Figures 4.10 to 4.13, which relate to both ordinary and rapid-hardening Portland cement and to both irregular gravel and crushed granite coarse aggregate with natural sand. For mixes made with coarse and fine crushed rock aggregate, values intermediate between those shown for gravel and granite would probably be attained.

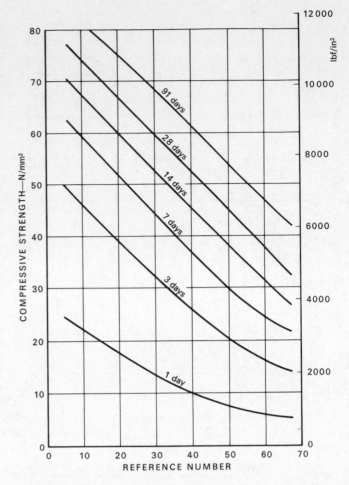

Figure 4.11 : Relation between compressive strength and reference number of concrete made from crushed granite coarse aggregate, natural sand and ordinary Portland cement.

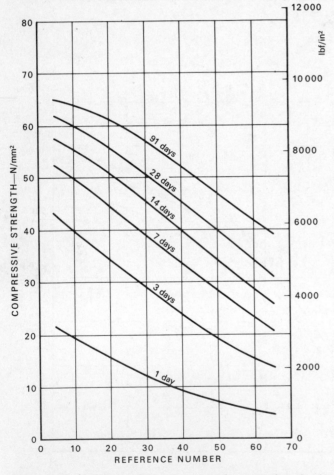

Figure 4.10 : Relation between compressive strength and reference number of concrete made from irregular gravel coarse aggregate, natural sand and ordinary Portland cement.

The 'reference numbers' have to be used to determine the water/cement ratio of the concrete, but before this can be done it is necessary to establish both the maximum size of the aggregate to be used and the workability of the concrete.

Data are included for maximum aggregate sizes of 10 mm (3/8 in.) and 20 mm (¾ in.). Similar data have not been produced for concretes containing aggregate of 40 mm (1½ in.) maximum size. In the absence of such data it is suggested that, for the purpose of making trial mixes, a sufficiently accurate estimate could be obtained by using the same data as for 20 mm (¾ in.) maximum size aggregate. The maximum size of aggregate appears to become less important as concrete compressive strength increases, probably because the 'ceiling' strength for any particular type of aggregate is slightly lower for a larger maximum size than for a smaller maximum size.

As mentioned earlier, concretes of high workability do not have such high strength as concretes of lower workability, and therefore the degree of workability described as 'high' in Table 4.2 is not used. Lower workabilities are, however, advantageous from the mix design point of view, and so a further category of 'extremely low' is included. This degree of workability is about the lowest at which the concrete can be compacted by intensive vibration above; lower values are likely to involve the use of pressure as well as vibration. In judging the required workability for high-strength concretes, some care must be exercised because these concretes tend to be required in narrow sections where access and compaction are not easy. Further, the lower the workability of the concrete, the longer compaction is likely to take and the greater the formwork pressures are likely to be.

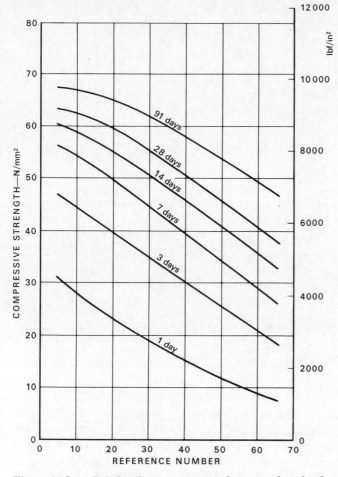

Figure 4.12 : Relation between compressive strength and reference number of concrete made from irregular gravel coarse aggregate, natural sand and rapid-hardening Portland cement.

The mixes being considered are generally of high cement content and low workability and they are therefore likely to be cohesive; thus there is little likelihood of segregation during handling or compaction. All the data therefore apply to aggregates of grading number 1 (Figures 4.3 and 4.4). Mixes at the lean end of the range considered therefore tend to be a little harsh, whereas those at the richer end tend to be a little too cohesive. This can usually be adjusted quite simply in trial mixes by increasing or decreasing the proportion of fine aggregate to total aggregate by up to 5%. Such changes generally have an unimportant effect on the measured values of compressive strength or compacting factor.

Once the maximum size of the aggregate and the workability of the concrete have been selected, the 'reference number' can be used to determine the total water/cement ratio (see Chapter 1.6) from Figures 4.14 and 4.15. This completes all the data required to determine the estimated aggregate/cement ratio by weight from Table 4.12 or 4.13. Batch weights should then be calculated and trial mixes

made, as described in Chapter 7. Strictly speaking, just before this is done, the proportions determined should be checked against the durability requirements which are discussed in Chapter 5; however, with concretes of the strengths being discussed, it is most unlikely that the durability requirements will show that a higher cement content or a lower water/cement ratio is needed.

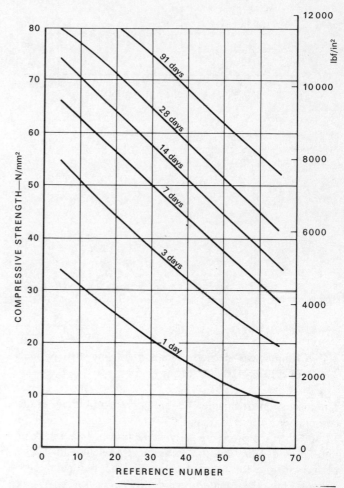

Figure 4.13 : Relation between compressive strength and reference number of concrete made from crushed granite coarse aggregate, natural sand and rapid-hardening Portland cement.

In practice, it is often advisable to complete the mix design procedure discussed for more than one type of cement and aggregate and for more than one degree of workability. This is because the initial choice of constituent materials and the degree of workability may show that they are not suitable. The choice may then be, for example, to use a lower workability than originally intended, or to import a crushed rock aggregate for use in preference to a local gravel aggregate. A further alternative may be to incorporate a water-reducing admixture, as will be discussed in Chapter 6.12.

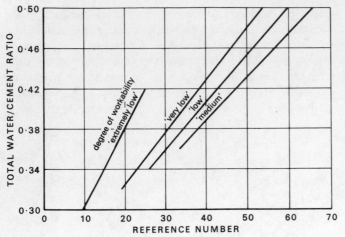

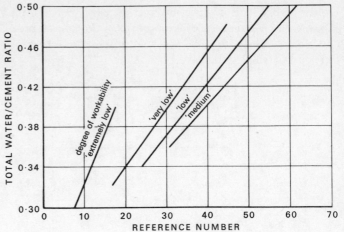

Figure 4.14 : Relation between reference number and total water/cement ratio of concrete made with 10 mm (3/8 in.) maximum-size aggregate.

Figure 4.15 : Relation between reference number and total water/cement ratio of concrete made with 20 mm (¾ in.) maximum-size aggregate.

4.6 Compressive strength between 80 and 110 N/mm² (11 500 and 16 000 lbf/in²)

The discussion in Chapter 4.5 on the design of mixes in the compressive strength range 45 to 80 N/mm² (6500 to 11 500 lbf/in²) showed clearly that published data were of only limited value and that considerable reliance had to be placed on previous experience with the particular constituent materials under consideration, or on trial mix results. This situation applies even more forcibly in the compressive strength range 80 to 110 N/mm² (11 500 to 16 000 lbf/in²).

Data currently available are not sufficient for a full mix design procedure to be developed. Work by Parrott[38, 39] does, however, give considerable information from which some guidance regarding mix proportions can be gained. There seems little benefit in producing concretes with an aggregate/cement ratio less than 2 by weight; this is substantially richer than is used in practice for high-strength prestressed concrete, and the properties of such concretes and in particular the evolution of heat of hydration should be carefully considered before the use of such mixes is agreed. From the point of view of construction, concretes of this type are liable to involve considerable changes in the methods of mixing, placing and compacting and in the rate of working. Apart from the cost of the constituents, the cost of producing and placing the concrete is likely to be relatively high.

Tables 4.14 and 4.15 give some details of the properties of the cements and aggregates used in Parrott's investi-gation, and Tables 4.16 and 4.17 show the effects of these various materials on the properties of concrete for which the aggregate/cement ratio was 2 by weight, the water/cement ratio was 0.28 and the fine aggregate — a natural sand — was 10% by weight of the total aggregate. The effect of the source of both the cement and the aggregate on the properties of the concrete can be seen to be considerable, and it is therefore advisable, when making trial mixes for any particular project, to use a range of constituent materials. When the trial mix results are available the most appropriate constituent materials may be selected, even though this may involve what would normally be regarded as an excessively long haul for delivering materials to the site.

Parrott concluded that it was possible to produce concrete with compressive strengths of 73, 88 and 97 N/mm² (10 600, 12 800 and 14 000 lbf/in²) at 7, 28 and 90 days respectively with a range of constituents, though a careful selection was necessary to achieve compressive strengths of 81, 101 and 110 N/mm² (11 700, 14 700 and 15 900 lbf/in²) at these respective ages.

All the aggregates examined were crushed rocks of 10 mm (3/8 in.) maximum size; because of the probably lower 'ceiling' strength of aggregates of larger maximum size, it is suggested that this size should preferably be used. Some adjustment of the data in Tables 4.16 and 4.17 can be made from the fact that a change of 0.1 in the water/cement ratio results in a change of compressive strength of nearly 20 N/mm² (2900 lbf/in²), assuming the concrete is fully compacted.

TABLE 4.12
Aggregate/cement ratios required to give four degrees of workability with different water/cement ratios, using ordinary Portland cement.

		Aggregate/cement ratio by weight															
Type of coarse aggregate*		Irregular gravel								Crushed granite							
Maximum size of aggregate		10 mm (3/8 in.)				20 mm (¾ in.)				10 mm (3/8 in.)				20 mm (¾ in.)			
Degree of workability†		EL	VL	L	M	EL	VL	L	M	EL	VL	L	M	EL	VL	L	M
Total water/cement	0.30	2.4				3.0				2.9				3.3			
ratio by weight	0.32	3.2				3.8	2.5			3.6	2.3			4.0	2.6		
	0.34	3.9	2.6			4.5	3.0	2.5		4.2	2.8	2.3		4.6	3.2	2.6	
	0.36	4.6	3.1	2.6		5.2	3.5	3.0	2.5	4.7	3.2	2.7	2.3	5.2	3.6	3.1	2.6
	0.38	5.2	3.5	3.0	2.5		4.0	3.4	2.9	5.2	3.6	3.0	2.6		4.1	3.5	2.9
	0.40		3.9	3.3	2.7		4.4	3.8	3.2		4.0	3.3	2.9		4.5	3.8	3.2
	0.42		4.3	3.6	3.0		4.9	4.1	3.5		4.4	3.6	3.1		4.9	4.2	3.5
	0.44		4.7	3.9	3.3		5.3	4.5	3.8		4.8	3.9	3.3		5.3	4.5	3.7
	0.46		5.1	4.2	3.6			4.8	4.1		5.1	4.2	3.6			4.8	4.0
	0.48		5.4	4.5	3.8			5.2	4.4		5.5	4.5	3.8			5.1	4.2
	0.50			4.8	4.1			5.5	4.7			4.7	4.0			5.4	4.5

Values in this table refer to grading No. 1 of Figures 4.3 and 4.4 for each maximum size.

*Natural sand used in combination with both types of coarse aggregate.

†EL = 'extremely low'
VL = 'very low'   } as defined in Table 4.2.
L = 'low'
M = 'medium'

TABLE 4.13
Aggregate/cement ratios required to give four degrees of workability with different water/cement ratios, using rapid-hardening Portland cement.

		Aggregate/cement ratio by weight															
Type of coarse aggregate*		Irregular gravel								Crushed granite							
Maximum size of aggregate		10 mm (3/8 in.)				20 mm (¾ in.)				10 mm (3/8 in.)				20 mm (¾ in.)			
Degree of workability†		EL	VL	L	M	EL	VL	L	M	EL	VL	L	M	EL	VL	L	M
Total water/cement	0.32					2.6				2.5				2.9			
ratio by weight	0.34	2.8				3.4	2.2			3.2				3.6	2.4		
	0.36	3.5	2.4			4.1	2.7	2.3		3.9	2.5			4.3	2.9	2.4	
	0.38	4.2	2.9	2.4		4.8	3.2	2.8	2.3	4.5	3.0	2.5		4.9	3.4	2.9	2.4
	0.40	4.9	3.3	2.8	2.3	5.5	3.7	3.2	2.7	5.0	3.4	2.9	2.4	5.5	3.9	3.3	2.7
	0.42		3.7	3.1	2.6		4.2	3.6	3.0	5.5	3.8	3.2	2.7		4.2	3.6	3.0
	0.44		4.1	3.5	2.9		4.6	4.0	3.4		4.2	3.5	3.0		4.7	4.0	3.3
	0.46		4.5	3.8	3.2		5.0	4.3	3.7		4.6	3.8	3.2		5.1	4.3	3.6
	0.48		4.9	4.1	3.5		5.5	4.7	4.0		5.0	4.1	3.4		5.5	4.6	3.9
	0.50		5.2	4.4	3.7			5.0	4.3		5.3	4.4	3.7			4.9	4.1

Values in this table refer to grading No. 1 of Figures 4.3 and 4.4 for each maximum size.

*Natural sand used in combination with both types of coarse aggregate.

†EL = 'extremely low'
VL = 'very low'   } as defined in Table 4.2.
L = 'low'
M = 'medium'

TABLE 4.14
Data on cements used in very high strength concrete mixes.

Cement	Computed composition – %				Na_2O – %	K_2O – %	Specific gravity	Specific surface – m^2/kg
	C_3S	C_2S	C_3A	C_4AF				
D (OPC)	40	38	8	5	0.17	0.54	3.17	367
E (OPC)	57	16	9	7	0.26	0.64	3.13	320
F (SRPC)	50	16	0	14	0.11	0.35	3.19	319
G (OPC)	64	17	7	5	0.25	0.59	3.12	298
H (OPC)	52	19	12	7	0.23	0.72	3.12	360
I (OPC)	33	38	10	5	0.15	0.73	3.04	435
J (OPC)	52	22	9	7	0.18	0.54	3.08	365
K (SRPC)	no data available							

Notes
OPC = ordinary Portland cement.
SRPC = sulphate-resisting Portland cement.

TABLE 4.15
Data on angular coarse aggregates of 10 to 5 mm (3/8 to 3/16 in.) size used in very high strength concrete mixes.

Aggregate	County	Description	Colour	Absorption after 1 hour – %	Specific gravity
Holcombe limestone	Somerset	carboniferous	medium grey	0.81	2.68
Mountsorrel soda granite	Leicestershire	igneous, acid, major intrusive	speckled pink	0.79	2.68
Swinburne quartz dolerite	Northumberland	ingeneous, intermediate, minor instrusive	dark grey	0.84	2.88
Bolam porhyritic basalt	Durham	igneous, basic, extrusive	dark grey	0.80	2.74
Clicker Tor picrite	Cornwall	igneous, ultra-basic, major intrusive	dark blue-grey	0.70	2.75
Dean gabbro	Cornwall	igneous, basic, major intrusive	blue-grey	0.63	2.86
Darby Hill olivine basalt	Staffordshire	igneous, basic, extrusive	medium-dark grey	1.20	2.77
Criggon albitized olivine basalt	Montgomery	igneous, basic, minor intrusive	green	1.15	2.69
Clee Hill olivine dolerite	Shropshire	igneous, basic, minor intrusive	dark grey	0.47	2.86

TABLE 4.16
Effect of cement in very high strength concrete mixes.

Cement	Aggregate	Vebe time (s)	Compressive strength – N/mm² (lbf/in²)		
			7 days	28 days	90 days
D	Holcombe limestone	15	72 (10 400)	83 (12 100)	91 (13 200)
E		13	73 (10 600)	88 (12 800)	95 (13 800)
F		10	70 (10 200)	90 (13 100)	96 (13 900)
G		23	76 (11 000)	85 (12 300)	93 (13 400)
H		15	71 (10 400)	78 (11 300)	89 (12 800)
I		37	66 (9 600)	78 (11 300)	84 (12 200)
K		16	74 (10 800)	91 (13 100)	98 (14 200)
D	Swinburne dolerite	18	73 (10 600)	93 (13 400)	101 (14 700)
E		12	81 (11 700)	100 (14 500)	110 (15 900)
F		12	71 (10 400)	93 (13 500)	106 (15 400)
J		12	78 (11 300)	92 (13 300)	102 (14 800)
D	Bolam basalt	30	73 (10 600)	91 (13 200)	103 (14 900)
E		12	82 (11 900)	102 (14 800)	109 (15 800)
F		13	72 (10 500)	89 (12 900)	102 (14 800)

TABLE 4.17
Effect of aggregate type in very high strength concrete mixes.

Cement	Aggregate	Vebe time (s)	Compressive strength – N/mm² (lbf/in²)		
			7 days	28 days	90 days
D	Clee Hill dolerite	22	69 (10 100)	84 (12 200)	93 (13 400)
D	Criggion dolerite	19	71 (10 300)	86 (12 400)	99 (14 400)
D	Darby Hill basalt	20	69 (10 000)	83 (12 000)	88 (12 800)
D	Dean gabbro	27	–	81 (11 800)	91 (13 200)
D	Clicker Tor picrite	18	72 (10 400)	83 (12 000)	90 (13 000)
D	Bolam basalt	30	73 (10 600)	91 (13 200)	103 (14 900)
D	Swinburne dolerite	18	73 (10 600)	92 (13 400)	101 (14 700)
D	Holcombe limestone	15	72 (10 400)	83 (12 100)	91 (13 200)
E	Bolam basalt	12	82 (11 900)	102 (14 800)	109 (15 800)
E	Swinburne dolerite	12	81 (11 700)	100 (14 500)	110 (15 900)
E	Holcombe limestone	13	73 (10 600)	88 (12 800)	95 (13 800)
E	Mountsorrel granite	17	75 (10 900)	90 (13 000)	97 (14 000)
F	Bolam basalt	13	72 (10 500)	89 (12 900)	102 (14 800)
F	Swinburne dolerite	12	71 (10 400)	93 (13 500)	106 (15 400)
F	Holcombe limestone	10	70 (10 200)	90 (13 100)	96 (13 900)

4.7 Compressive strength over 110 N/mm² (16 000 lbf/in²)

Concretes having strengths greater than 110 N/mm² (16 000 lbf/in²) have been produced in the laboratory but cannot yet be regarded as practicable in normal construction work. The techniques usually involve cements other than Portland cements, cementitious or synthetic aggregate or methods of pressure compaction. The limiting strength of cement paste has been studied[40] using techniques of powder metallurgy to make compacts, under high pressure, of cement powder which is subsequently hydrated. These have produced strengths up to 375 N/mm² (54 000 lbf/in²) in compression and up to about 25 N/mm² (3600 lbf/in²) in tension, but this material cannot be classified as concrete.

4.8 Mix design for a range of mixes

4.8.1 Principles

The situation can arise, for example when a new ready mixed concrete plant is being set up, where data are required for many mixes covering a wide range of concrete properties. In this situation, trial mixes will certainly be made and the finally selected properties will depend on the results obtained. The selection of the mix proportions to be used for the trial mixes, however, requires some consideration. The following procedure has been adapted from one suggested by Owens[41] and is limited to that range of mixes most likely to be used in practice.

The procedure differs from those discussed in Chapters 4.4, 4.5 and 4.6 in that the strength of the concrete is considered last, rather than first, and the initial aim is to produce concretes of good workability characteristics having a range of cement contents. When the trial mix results for compressive strength are available, it is then possible to determine the minimum strengths for which particular values of cement content would be appropriate.

4.8.2 Aggregates

A survey of locally available aggregate supplies will probably show that one particular geological type of aggregate must be used. In the unlikely event of two basically different types of aggregate being available, the whole procedure should be completed for both types; the final choice of which material to use will probably be based on the relative cost of the concrete made with each type of material.

The first choice open is probably whether to use graded or single-sized coarse aggregates. From the technical point of view of producing the most uniform concrete, the latter is more likely to be better; this would ultimately be reflected in the standard deviation of compressive strength test results obtained from routine work. The use of graded coarse aggregate is, however, quite satisfactory for a wide range of work, and has the economic advantage of there being only one size of coarse aggregate to store, handle and batch. If past test results of the grading of the various sizes of coarse aggregate are available, this will clearly assist in choosing the best combination of material for the purpose of making the trial mixes.

If single-sized coarse aggregates are to be used, the proportions in which they can generally be combined are in the ratio of 2 to 1 by weight for any size to the single size immediately smaller. Thus, if two sizes were used, say 20 to 10 mm (¾ to 3/8 in.) and 10 to 5 mm (3/8 to 3/16 in.), the percentages by total weight of coarse aggregate would be 67 to 33; similarly, if three sizes, namely 37.5 to 20 mm (1½ to ¾ in.), 20 to 10 mm (¾ to 3/8 in.) and 10 to 5 mm (3/8 to 3/16 in.), were to be used, the proportions would be 57, 29 and 14% respectively. If a more precise answer is required which takes over-size and under-size material in each size into account, this can be obtained by adopting the procedure discussed in Chapter 7.2.1.

The next stage is to determine the proportion of fine to total aggregate. Ideally this value depends on many factors, including the maximum size and particle shape of the coarse aggregate, the grading of the fine aggregate, the workability of the concrete, the cement content of the mix and the conditions under which the concrete is to be placed; the value finally selected will depend upon the trial mix results, though values can initially be selected from Table 4.18, which gives suggested proportions of fine aggregate as percentages by weight of total aggregate for concrete made with dense aggregate of 20 mm (¾ in.) nominal maximum size, of medium workability, and with a cement content of about 300 kg/m³ (500 lb/yd³). For concrete containing aggregate of 40 mm (1½ in.) nominal maximum size, the values can be reduced by 5% (but not to below 20%), and for 10 mm (3/8 in.) maximum size aggregate the values should be increased by 5%. Where concrete is of high workability the values should be increased by 5%, and where the workability is lower than medium it may be possible to reduce the values slightly, but not to below 20%.

TABLE 4.18

Guide to the proportions of fine aggregate in total aggregate for trial mixes, using a maximum size of aggregate of 20 mm (¾ in.) in concrete of medium workability and containing about 300 kg/m³ (500 lb/yd³) of cement.

Fine aggregate zone	Predominant particle shape of coarse aggregate		
	Rounded	Irregular	Angular
1	35 – 40	40 – 45	45 – 50
2	30 – 35	35 – 40	35 – 45
3	25 – 30	30 – 35	30 – 40
4	20 – 25	25 – 30	25 – 30

4.8.3 First trial mix

The first trial mix using air-dried aggregates should aim to produce a concrete having a cement content about 300 kg/m³ (500 lb/yd³), but since the amount of mixing water required to produce the required workability (which may be taken as 'medium') is not known and it is highly likely that the specific gravity of the fine and coarse aggregate are not known, it is reasonable to adopt an aggregate/cement ratio of 6 by weight. Thus the weights of all the solid constituents can be calculated and trial mixes can be made in accordance with Chapter 7.3.2. The only unknown is the amount of water needed to give the concrete the required medium workability. This must be judged initially by eye and then measured; if necessary, several trial mixes should be made until the required value is obtained. Once a satisfactory value has been obtained, the other tests on the concrete, for fresh density and compressive strength, can proceed. The quantity of water batched can be measured and, from separate tests to determine the absorption characteristics of the aggregate, the free water/cement ratio can be determined.

All the data necessary for the determination of the cement content and water content are now available and it is now possible to start entering the data on Figure 4.16. An ordinate can be drawn on the strength graph opposite the cement content used and, just below this value, the water content in litres/m³ (gal/yd³) and the weights of the various sizes of fine and coarse aggregates in kg/m³ (lb/yd³) can be written.

4.8.4 Subsequent trial mixes

Now that the amount of water required to produce a concrete of medium workability using the constituent materials intended for full-scale working has been determined, it is possible to produce a range of concrete mixes. The proportions selected will depend upon the circumstances, though aggregate/cement ratios of 3, 4.5 and 7.5 may be appropriate for many practical circumstances. The proportion of fine aggregate in the total aggregate could be adjusted from the value selected for the first mix by −4%, −2% and +2% respectively for the three further mixes just suggested.

The making of these further trial mixes is considerably eased by the fact that the free water content, in units of litres/m³ (gal/yd³), is likely to remain sensibly constant over the range of mixes being considered and will produce concretes of similar workability. Therefore, if the volume of concrete produced in each trial mix is the same, the quantity of water added at the mixer will be virtually constant. The data obtained during the making of the trial mixes are then entered in the lower part of Figure 4.16.

Trial mixes can also be made using maximum sizes of aggregate other than 20 mm (¾ in.). As a guide to the amount of mixing water required to achieve the same workability as that obtained with 20 mm aggregate

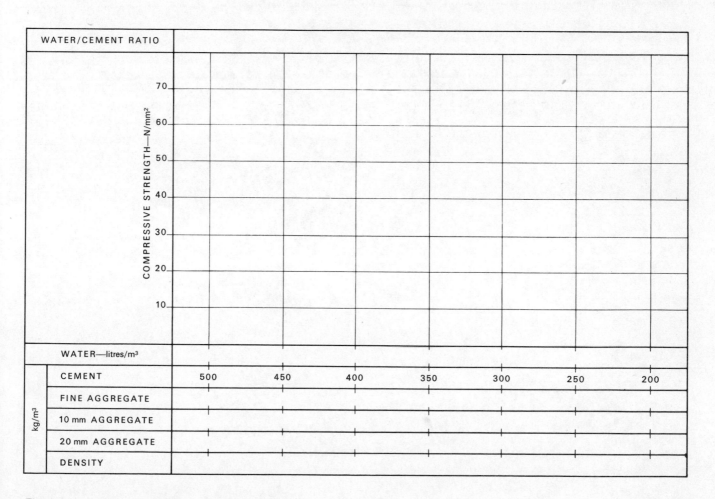

Figure 4.16 : Chart for the design of a range of mixes.

concrete, about 12% more water will be required when 10 mm (3/8 in.) aggregate is used and about 12% less when nominal 40 mm (1½ in.) aggregate is used.

4.8.5 Strength test results

As the strength test results become available they can be entered in the graphical section of Figure 4.16. These results will generally be at ages of 7 and 28 days, though there is no reason why other ages should not be included. It would also be appropriate to enter any accelerated cube test results[42, 43] which might be required to obtain early data, either for quality control or to comply with a specification.

Once the data are substantially complete, graphs of strength against cement content can be drawn, and any 'rogue' results can be detected and either repeated or neglected.

At this stage, it is unlikely that the efficiency of quality control measures will have been assessed in terms of the compressive test results obtained in the course of normal work. It would therefore be necessary to assume that a margin of 15 N/mm² (2200 lbf/in² (or less in the case of low-strength mixes) will be needed (see Chapter 4.2). Thus, to meet a particular specified characteristic strength, a curve 15 N/mm² (2200 lbf/in²) lower than that drawn

from the trial mix test results will have to be drawn. Appropriate mix proportions can then be interpolated from the data in the lower part of Figure 4.16. As long as durability requirements are not over-riding, these values can then be used for full-scale work.

4.8.6 Concrete production

During the course of full-scale work, test results will become available from which it may be necessary to modify the data in Figure 4.16. Firstly, the level of quality control being achieved will be assessed probably in terms of the standard deviation of test results, and a modified margin between the specified and target mean strength will be justified (see Chapter 4.2). Secondly, strengths rather different from those obtained during the trials may occur. This could be due to a change in the quality of the constituent material, in which case a modified relation between strength and cement content should be drawn. This modified relation is not likely to be so seriously different from the first relation that sub-standard concrete will be produced; uncertainty about the initial data is one of the reasons why the margins given in Chapter 4.2 are adopted. The possible need to change mix proportions during the course of production is discussed more fully in Chapter 7.

CHAPTER 5

Mix design for durability

5.1 General

Durability is a general term which, when applied to concrete, means the ability of the material to fulfil its required function throughout the life of the structure in which it has been used without losing structural strength or appearance.

The fact that concrete is generally a very durable material is probably responsible for the subject having received relatively little attention by concrete producers in the past. Nevertheless the subject does justify greater attention, particularly in regard to those aspects discussed in this chapter. The mechanisms by which concrete might prove not to be durable vary widely. To mention only three, there are frost damage, chemical attack and abrasion, each of which can, and often should, be sub-divided. Not only are there many mechanisms which should be considered when durability is assessed, but the concrete may prove to be more or less durable depending upon the environment in which it is kept; wet or dry, hot or cold, static or rapidly changing conditions. It is therefore incorrect to speak simply of durability without clarifying the forms of attack against which the concrete should be durable and the general environment in which the concrete is to be maintained.

There are several important aspects of durability which are related to the permeability of concrete. This aspect of the subject is therefore considered first.

5.2 Permeability

The permeability of concrete is of fundamental importance when the possibility of penetration by potentially aggressive chemicals, which may be either liquids or gases, is considered. Study of the structure of hardened cement-and-water paste has shown that the hydrated cement gel contains many very fine pores which have diameters around 0.015 μm and total some 28% by volume of the cement paste; these pores are so fine as to be virtually impermeable and do not generally need to be considered further. Capillary pores are considerably larger, having diameters up to about 5 μm, and will form anything up to 40% by volume of the cement paste, depending upon the water/cement ratio used and the extent of chemical hydration which has taken place.

Voids larger than capillary pores would generally be termed 'entrapped air', which is expected to occur in most concrete to the extent of 1 to 2% of the total volume. Recommendations regarding the design of concrete mixes generally assume this amount of entrapped air. Larger quantities of entrapped air, or voids resulting from inadequate compaction of the concrete, should clearly be avoided by good mix design, good quality control and good site supervision. Lightweight concretes form a separate category in this respect and are considered in Chapter 6.7.

From the point of view of obtaining low permeability, control over the volume of the capillary pores is most important. The significance of the water/cement ratio and the degree of hydration in exercising this control is illustrated in Figures 5.1 and 5.2.

In Figure 5.1 the quantity of water flowing per second through a given thickness of concrete has been measured and expressed as a coefficient,[44] K, in the expression:

$$\frac{dq}{dt}\frac{1}{A} = K\frac{\Delta h}{L}$$

where $\dfrac{dq}{dt}$ is the rate of flow of water in cm^3/s,

A is the cross-sectional area of the sample in cm^2,

Δh is the loss in hydraulic head through the sample in cm, and

L is the thickness of the sample in cm.

Although the data in Figure 5.1 apply to one particular cement, it has been shown that quite wide changes in the chemical composition and fineness of the cement have a relatively small effect on the coefficient of permeability when this is compared with the effect of changes in the water/cement ratio.

The important point to note is the very rapid increase in permeability at water/cement ratios above about 0.55. Whether the particular value of 0.55 can, from this particular piece of research, be taken as being significant in practice is not certain. Nevertheless, practical experience often suggests that this value should not be exceeded under particular conditions (see, for example, BS 340). The numerical values of Figure 5.2, also, should not be applied to practical conditions, though the very considerable effect the first few days of hydration have on the permeability should be noted as one of the justifications for good curing of concrete.[44]

The time necessary for cement paste, which has been kept continuously damp, to hydrate sufficiently for the capillary pores to be blocked has been investigated, and the figures given in Table 5.1 are suggested as being typical;[45] again,

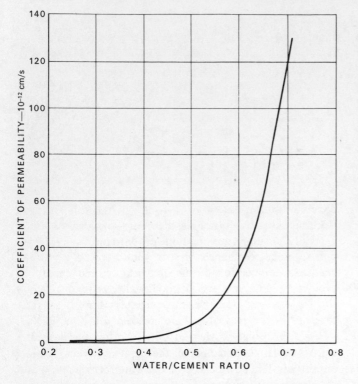

Figure 5.1 : Example of the relation between permeability and water/cement ratio for mature cement paste (93% of the cement hydrated).

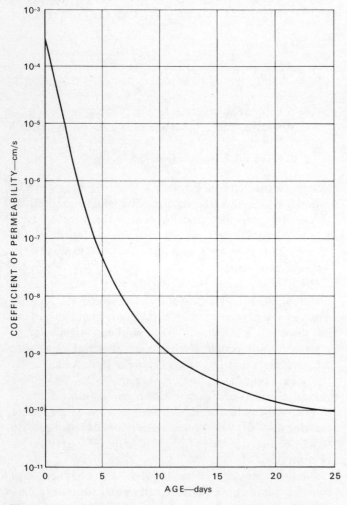

Figure 5.2 : Example of the reduction of permeability of cement paste by cement hydration (water/cement ratio 0.7).

the numerical values cannot be applied directly to practical conditions, although it is clear that water/cement ratios below 0.5 or 0.55 are needed in concrete where low permeability is necessary and where most of the normal drying out will occur in the first two months after casting. This consideration of capillary pore structure shows clearly that the two factors of water/cement ratio and degree of hydration have a major effect on the permeability of concrete. an adequate degree of hydration is generally obtained in practice, either by the thickness of concrete being sufficient to ensure that the bulk of the concrete remains damp for the requisite time, or by the concrete being kept in a damp environment, or by good curing; these are matters beyond the scope of this book and are therefore not considered further. The water/cement ratio is, however, of primary importance.

TABLE 5.1
Relation between age of concrete at which capillary pores become blocked and water/cement ratio.

Water/cement ratio	Age of concrete at which capillary pores become blocked
0.4	3 days
0.45	7 days
0.5	14 days
0.6	6 months
0.7	1 year
over 0.7	infinity

As has already been discussed, the accurate measurement of water/cement ratio on site is difficult, due partly to variations in the moisture content of aggregates, partly to an inability to measure the quantity of water in fresh concrete under most practical conditions, and partly to problems associated with the absorption of water by the aggregates. However, for a given maximum size and type of aggregate and a given workability of concrete, the quantity of water per unit volume of compacted concrete is reasonably constant over a wide range of cement contents. Therefore it is reasonable, in practice, to ensure that the cement content used exceeds a particular minimum value which has been determined in such a way that the maximum water/cement ratio is unlikely to exceed the value which it has been found necessary, from considerations of permeability and past experience, not to exceed. Control over the maximum water/cement ratio is, in effect, maintained via control over the batch weights of the constituents and the workability of the concrete. Often recommendations to ensure adequate durability of concrete in service include a minimum cement content requirement, which can be verified on site at the time of batching and by analysing the freshly made concrete.

These durability requirements are additional to those of strength. It is important that the cement content actually used should be the higher of the value arrived at as a result of mix design for strength (see Chapter 4) and the minimum value specified for durability (Chapter 5). Aggregate/cement ratios and cement contents may be related either by calculation, using the specific gravity of the aggregate and the water/cement ratio, or by using Figure 2.1. In some cases — where exposure to sulphate-containing ground waters is under consideration, for example — the maximum water/cement ratio is laid down as well as the minimum cement content. Details of how this is applied in practice are included in Chapter 7.3.2.

5.3 Weathering and the protection of embedded metals[46, 47]

In normal good-quality work the effects of exposure to the atmosphere are not serious in the sense that the structure will fail, but rather that the appearance of the concrete may suffer and remedial work will be needed. Concrete is liable to contamination or to chemical attack from several sources to an extent dependent upon the permeability of the concrete. Water or water vapour is absorbed by the concrete, leading to dampness appearing on the surface, and it can take considerable time for the concrete to dry out again. The surface of the concrete might become carbonated by carbon dioxide in the atmosphere, which leads to a slight dusting. The concrete might be penetrated by atmospheric pollutants such as sulphur dioxide. Frequent wetting

and drying, combined with freezing and thawing, may cause slight surface breakdown which could be seen as surface crazing.

To these factors, none of which in itself is likely to be serious, must be added the more important point that the concrete should be required to give protection to all embedded metal and particularly to reinforcing and pre-stressing steel. To maintain the steel in good condition, moisture and air should be excluded; but as this is not completely possible the concrete is required to contain enough cement to provide an alkaline environment round the steel. This environment can be broken down

(1) by the concrete being sufficiently permeable as to permit significant penetration of the concrete by carbon dioxide;

(2) by a wide crack in the concrete which exposes the steel to the atmosphere; or

(3) by a minor crack which accelerates carbonation in the vicinity of the crack.

Clearly, the avoidance of excessive cracking is largely a matter of structural design and reinforcement detailing but, nevertheless, the corrosion of the steel is likely to be confined to the proximity of the crack and is not likely to be so serious as a more widespread condition where the

TABLE 5.2 (metric units)
Minimum cement content (kg/m^3) required in Portland cement concrete of characteristic compressive strength of 20 N/mm^2 or more, to ensure durability.

Exposure	Reinforced concrete Nominal maximum size of aggregate — mm				Prestressed concrete Nominal maximum size of aggregate — mm				Plain concrete Nominal maximum size of aggregate — mm			
	40	20	14	10	40	20	14	10	40	20	14	10
mild — for example, completely protected against weather or aggresive conditions, except for a brief period of exposure to normal weather conditions during construction	220	250	270	290	300	300	300	300	200	220	250	270
moderate — for example, sheltered from severe rain and against freezing while saturated with water. Buried concrete and concrete continuously under water.	260	290	320	340	300	300	320	340	220	250	280	300
severe — for example, exposed to sea water, moorland water, driving rain, alternate wetting and drying and to freezing while wet. Subject to heavy condensation or corrosive fumes	320	360	390	410	320	360	390	410	270	310	330	360
subject to salt used for de-icing	260	290	320	340	300	300	320	340	240	280	310	330

When the maximum free water/cement ratio can be strictly controlled these may be reduced to:

Exposure	Reinforced concrete Nominal maximum size of aggregate — mm				Maximum water/ cement ratio	Prestressed concrete Nominal maximum size of aggregate — mm				Maximum water/ cement ratio	Plain concrete Nominal maximum size of aggregate — mm				Maximum water/ cement ratio
	40	20	14	10		40	20	14	10		40	20	14	10	
mild	200	230	250	260	0.65	300	300	300	300	0.65	180	200	220	240	0.70
moderate	240	260	290	310	0.55	300	300	300	310	0.55	200	230	250	270	0.60
severe	290	330	350	370	0.45	300	330	350	370	0.45	240	280	300	320	0.50
salt used for de-icing	240	260	290	310	0.55	300	300	300	310	0.55	220	250	280	300	0.55

permeability of the concrete is excessive. Further, there is reason to believe that the width of a crack is often directly proportional to the cover and so diminishes to nothing near the reinforcement; if this is generally true (it cannot be true for all circumstances such as cracking resulting from gross over-dosage of calcium chloride), then the permeability of the concrete again becomes the more important factor. The protection of embedded metals therefore comes down, firstly, to providing the concrete with a sufficiently high cement content to avoid excessive permeability and to give adequate alkalinity and, secondly, to ensuring adequate cover to the metal.

Recommended values of minimum cement content and maximum water/cement ratio for reinforced, prestressed and plain concrete made with Portland cement are given in Table 5.2, which is taken from CP 110; the values are appropriate for the large majority of natural aggregates available in the United Kingdom. Under each condition of exposure and maximum size of aggregate, two values of minimum cement content are given; the first refers to the condition where the maximum water/cement ratio is not checked, and the second to the condition where there is every reason to suppose that the free water/cement ratio given is not being exceeded. The following further points apply to the table.

(1) For concretes of lower minimum or characteristic strength, lower cement contents can be used, namely:

Characteristic strength— N/mm^2 (lbf/in^2)	Minimum cement content— kg/m^3 (lb/yd^3)
7 (1000)	120 (200)
10 (1450)	150 (250)
15 (2200)	180 (300)

(2) Concrete of characteristic strength 40 N/mm^2 (5800 lbf/in^2) or lower should be air-entrained where de-icing salt is to be used (see Chapter 6.5).

Table 5.3, the data for which have also been taken from CP 110, shows the lowest characteristic compressive strength advisable for particular exposure conditions where the nominal cover has already been fixed from other considerations.

5.4 Sulphates in the soil or ground water

Where hardened Portland cement concrete is exposed to soil or ground water containing sulphate compounds, the sulphates in solution are likely to react with the hydrated tricalcium aluminate in the hardened cement paste to form

TABLE 5.2 (imperial units)
Minimum cement content (lb/yd^3) required in Portland cement concrete of characteristic compressive strength of 2900 lbf/in^2 or more, to ensure durability.

Exposure	Reinforced concrete Nominal maximum size of aggregate – in.				Prestressed concrete Nominal maximum size of aggregate – in.				Plain concrete Nominal maximum size of aggregate – in.			
	1½	¾	½	3/8	1½	¾	½	3/8	1½	¾	½	3/8
mild – for example, completely protected against weather or aggressive conditions, except for a brief period of exposure to normal weather conditions during construction	370	420	455	490	505	505	505	505	335	370	420	455
moderate – for example, sheltered from severe rain and against freezing while saturated with water. Buried concrete and concrete continuously under water	440	490	540	570	505	505	540	570	370	420	470	505
severe – for example, exposed to sea water, moorland water, driving rain, alternate wetting and drying and to freezing while wet. Subject to heavy condensation or corrosive fumes	540	605	660	695	540	605	660	695	455	520	555	605
subject to salt used for de-icing	440	490	540	570	505	505	540	570	405	470	520	555

When the maximum free water/cement ratio can be strictly controlled these may be reduced to:

Exposure	Reinforced concrete Nominal maximum size of aggregate – in.				Maximum water/ cement ratio	Prestressed concrete Nominal maximum size of aggregate – in.				Maximum water/ cement ratio	Plain concrete Nominal maximum size of aggregate – in.				Maximum water/ cement ratio
	1½	¾	½	3/8		1½	¾	½	3/8		1½	¾	½	3/8	
mild	335	390	420	440	0.65	505	505	505	505	0.65	305	335	370	405	0.70
moderate	405	440	490	520	0.55	505	505	505	520	0.55	335	390	420	455	0.60
severe	490	555	590	625	0.45	505	555	590	625	0.45	405	470	505	540	0.50
salt used for de-icing	405	440	490	520	0.55	505	505	505	520	0.55	370	420	470	505	0.55

a new chemical called ettringite; in extreme cases this can cause expansion and disruption of the concrete. It is therefore necessary to limit the permeability of the concrete, to an extent dependent upon the concentration of the sulphates, so as to reduce the penetration of the aggressive liquid into the concrete. With the higher sulphate concentrations it is necessary to use a cement with higher resistance to sulphates, that is sulphate-resisting Portland cement in which a strict limit is imposed on the tricalcium aluminate content, or to use supersulphated or high alumina cement.

Recommendations for cement type, minimum cement content and maximum water/cement ratio are given in Table 5.4. This has been partly taken from the Building Research Station Digest 90 (2nd series)[48] to which reference should be made for further details, particularly concerning the method of sampling the ground and ground water and the interpretation of the results. The 40 mm (1½ in.) and 10 mm (3/8 in.) values for maximum aggregate sizes have been extrapolated from the values for 20 mm (¾ in.) given in the Digest. It should be noted that the table includes requirements for cement content and water/cement ratio, which should both be checked carefully on site in advance of construction work. The use of calcium chloride is not recommended.

Interpretation of data of this type must be carefully considered in relation to site conditions. For example, flowing ground water is liable to be more damaging than static water as the sulphate will be replenished. Also, water pressure on one side of a structure may be more damaging than equal pressure all round.

The most widespread salts are calcium sulphate (gypsum or selenite), magnesium sulphate (Epsom salt) and sodium sulphate (Glauber salt). Of these calcium sulphate is the least soluble, dissolving to only 1.2 g (SO_3) per litre or 120 parts per 100 000. If it is known that, in a particular area, sulphates are attributable to the calcium salt alone, then a solution of not more than this concentration can be assumed when referring to Table 5.4.

5.5 Sea water

Good quality concrete resists sea water well despite the fact that, in theory, sulphate attack should occur in concrete members placed in the sea, where the SO_3 content is about 210 parts per 100 000, in the same way as sulphate attack might be expected in land conditions. In practice, however, some of the expansive compounds are leached out and damage by expansion is unlikely. Instead, the magnesium

TABLE 5.3
Lowest characteristic compressive strength recommended for particular conditions of exposure and nominal cover to reinforcement.

Exposure	Lowest characteristic compressive strength – N/mm² (lbf/in²)						
	Nominal cover†						
	15 mm (0.6 in.)	20 mm (0.8 in.)	25 mm (1.0 in.)	30 mm (1.2 in.)	40 mm (1.6 in.)	50 mm (2.0 in.)	60 mm (2.4 in.)
mild – for example, completely protected against weather or aggressive conditions, except for a brief period of exposure to normal weather conditions during construction	30 (4350)	25 (3600)	20 (2900)	20 (2900)	20 (2900)	20 (2900)	20 (2900)
moderate – for example, sheltered from severe rain and against freezing while saturated with water. Buried concrete and concrete continuously under water	NA	50 (7250)	40 (5800)	30 (4350)	25 (3600)	25 (3600)	25 (3600)
severe – for example, exposed to driving rain, alternate wetting and drying and to freezing while wet. Subject to heavy condensation or corrosive fumes	NA	NA	50 (7250)	40 (5800)	30 (4350)	25 (3600)	25 (3600)
very severe – exposed to sea water or moorland water and with abrasion	NA	NA	NA	NA	NA	50 (7250)	40 (5800)
subject to salt used for de-icing	NA	NA	50 (7250)	50 (7250)	40* (5800*)	30* (4350*)	30* (4350*)

NA indicates that the combination of strength and cover is not advised.

* Only applicable if the concrete has entrained air.

† These values should be increased by 10 mm (0.3 in.) whenever the table is applied to lightweight aggregate concrete, except for internal non-corrosive conditions.

salts in the sea water are liable to convert some of the calcium silicate compounds in the hardened cement paste into magnesium silicates, which are relatively weak. The effect, therefore, is one of a slight weakening of the surface of the concrete. For practical purposes this can be overcome by complying with the recommendations for 'severe' expsoure given in Table 5.2. In addition, it is a wise precaution to use a sulphate-resisting Portland cement rather than an ordinary or rapid-hardening Portland cement.

5.6   Acids and alkalis

Portland cement concrete is essentially an alkaline material which is generally stable within a range of pH 7 to pH 12.5. It is possible to expose it to liquids and vapours outside these limits, extending the range to perhaps pH 6 to pH 13, as any attack which takes place on dense concrete is likely to be so slow as still to give the concrete an adequate life.

Several practical solutions to potential acid attack are possible, including the isolation of the concrete from the acid and the neutralizing of the acid in the vicinity of the concrete. It is also possible to extend the life of the concrete itself under slightly acid conditions by careful selection of the type of aggregate used. If the concrete is to be placed in a situation where there is a limited amount of acid, which will not be replenished (for example by movement of ground water), then the use of a limestone aggregate which is itself attacked by acids will mean that the concrete is damaged to a shallower depth than if all the acid had been used up neutralizing the cement paste, as would happen with other types of aggregate; a sacrificial layer of extra concrete, perhaps 20 mm (¾ in.) thick, would probably be ample in many circumstances. Alternatively, if the acid is being continually replenished, it would probably be preferable to use a siliceous aggregate which is not attacked by the acid, so that, as the cement paste is eaten away, a higher proportion of aggregate will be exposed, so reducing the area over which the acid can attack; clearly, the attack will not be stopped, though the rate of attack might well be significantly reduced.

High alumina cement concrete tends to have better resistance to acids and can generally be used in the range pH 4 to pH 12, excluding mineral acids and caustic alkalis. Supersulphated cement concrete can generally withstand a wider range of pH 3 to pH 12. In all cases of potential acid attack the concretes should be made as dense as possible,

TABLE 5.4
Mix details for concrete exposed to sulphate attack.

Class	In soil			Mix details for dense, fully compacted concrete made with aggregates complying with BS 882 or BS 1047			
	Total SO₃ – %	SO₃ in 1 : 1 water extract – g/litre	Parts per 100 000	Type of cement	(a) Minimum cement content – kg/m³ (lb/yd³) Nominal maximum size of aggregate – mm (in.)		(b) Maximum free water/cement ratio
					40 (1½)	20 (¾)	10 (3/8)	
1	less than 0.2		less than 30	ordinary Portland or Portland-blastfurnace	240 (400)	280 (470)	330 (560) 0.55
2	0.2 to 0.5		30 to 120	ordinary Portland or Portland-blastfurnace	290 (490)	330 (560)	380 (640) 0.50
				sulphate-resisting Portland	240 (400)	280 (470)	330 (560) 0.55
				supersulphated	270 (450)	310 (520)	360 (610) 0.50
3	0.5 to 1.0	2.5 to 5.0	120 to 250	sulphate-resisting Portland or supersulphated	290 (490)	330 (560)	380 (640) 0.50
				high alumina	290 (490)	330 (560)	380 (640) 0.45
4	1.0 to 2.0	5.0 to 10.0	250 to 500	sulphate-resisting Portland or supersulphated	330 (560)	370 (620)	420 (710) 0.45
				high alumina	300 (510)	340 (570)	410 (690) 0.40
5	over 2	over 10	over 500	as for previous class plus adequate protective coatings, or high alumina	330 (560)	370 (620)	420 (710) 0.35

Note: Columns (a) and (b) *both* apply.

using a low water/cement ratio and good curing. With very strong acids, and some particular acids such as acetic acid, all hydraulic cement concretes will have to be protected by a membrane.

5.7 Frost and de-icing salts

Once good quality concrete has hardened for several days it is, in the vast majority of instances, immune from possible damage by frost. The situation where damage might occur are when either (1) the free water/cement ratio of the concrete was excessively high or (2) an unsuitable aggregate has been used; in both cases, however, the concrete would have to be in a saturated or nearly saturated condition when the frost occurs and the rate of freezing would have to be very fast. In practice these combinations do not often arise, and the possibility of frost damage is generally ignored for most work in the United Kingdom.

Several circumstances under which damage might occur do, however, merit further consideration. The free water/cement ratio beyond which damage is considered as possible is sometimes quoted as 0.55, for example in BS 340. Aggregates might prove unacceptable in two ways. Firstly, a few sources of material contain soft particles which have a high absorption; if the aggregate is saturated, and the concrete surrounding the aggregate particles is relatively dense, then, with fairly rapid freezing, the particles could expand beyond their original size as the water freezes into ice and so disrupt the concrete, probably causing small pop-outs on the surface. It should be noted that the aggregate must be fully or nearly fully saturated before damage can occur and that this is unlikely to happen, particularly with lightweight aggregate of high potential absorption.

The second circumstance is in paving work where very flaky aggregate particles might, as a result of the placing and compacting technique adopted, be oriented parallel to and near the surface of the concrete, so that subsequent bleeding of the mixing water causes a water cavity to be formed immediately below the particle; this cavity in the hardened concrete might subsequently become re-filled with water which could expand on freezing, so causing a pop-out. There is a further mechanism by which flaky aggregate particles near the surface may lead to pop-outs. If the hardened concrete is nearly fully saturated and is then frozen rapidly from the upper surface, the water at the very top of the concrete freezes first, so trapping the water beneath. As freezing continues, water is driven downwards; this continues until the freezing front reaches the upper surface of the flaky particle which is too impermeable to allow the water to pass through, so the accumulated water at the top of the particle then freezes, causing a pop-out which leaves the aggregate particle exposed.

The remedy to frost damage is therefore to avoid free water/cement ratios in excess of 0.55 and unusually flaky aggregate in circumstances where the hardened concrete might be rapidly frozen whilst already saturated or nearly so. There is, however, a more positive method by which potential frost damage can be avoided, and that is to use air entrainment.

Whereas air entrainment can be regarded as a wise precaution in the above circumstances, it can become essential in the potentially more damaging situation where frozen concrete is subject to treatment by salt (generally sodium chloride, though sometimes calcium chloride) for the purpose of de-icing.[11] In practice the situations in which damage by surface scaling can occur include, firstly, in situ concrete where salt is deliberately applied or is brought on to the concrete by vehicles and, secondly, roadside structures which might come into contact with salt solutions by splashing from passing vehicles or by run-off of drainage water containing salt. The former situation constitutes a potentially serious problem requiring the use of air-entrained concrete, whereas the latter situation does not often lead to damage and can generally be avoided by using a relatively high-strength concrete — with a minimum or characteristic strength of 50 N/mm^2 (7250 lbf/in2) and over at 28 days — in the first instance. The only exception to the need for air entrainment is in some precast concrete units where the concrete is hydraulically pressed (for example, paving flags and kerbs) or spun (for example, lamp standards), where exceptionally low free water/cement ratios are achieved due to the method of manufacture.

Where de-icing is carried out by other chemicals such as glycols, the need for air entrainment is less apparent, though it is probably still a wise precaution.

The nature of air entrainment was described in Chapter 3.4.6. Consideration of the subject now turns to the design of air-entrained concrete mixes (see Chapter 6.5).

Mix design for particular properties and purposes

6.1 General

There are many circumstances in which concrete is required to have particular properties other than, or in addition to, those of compressive strength, durability and workability which have been the primary concern of the two preceding chapters. In discussing these further properties, most of the previous discussion still applies and should be assumed to apply unless otherwise stated.

6.2 Flexural and tensile strength

The flexural and tensile strengths of concrete can be assessed by means of test beams broken in flexure or test cylinders crushed on their sides to give a splitting failure, the so-called indirect tensile strength. Both test procedures are given in BS 1881.

Whereas the cylinder splitting test is relatively new, the flexural test has been subject to slight modification from the procedure adopted in the earlier edition of the Standard; in particular, specimens are now required to be loaded on their sides as cast. There are therefore little or no data available, based on the latest agreed test procedures, to assist with the design of mixes for flexural or indirect tensile strength; also, the lack of clear definition in the Standard regarding the nature of the packing pieces to be used in the indirect tensile strength test leads to difficulty in interpreting past data. Until more data are available, initial mix designs can be made by converting the required flexural or indirect tensile strength into a compressive strength and then completing the mix design as explained in Chapter 4.

A relation between flexural and compressive strength test results is given in Figure 6.1 which has been derived from the work of several investigators.[39, 49, 50] One of those investigations[49] included concrete with and without entrained air; the air-entrained concrete had compressive strengths up to about 36 N/mm² (5200 lbf/in²). The considerable width of the bands of test results associated with each type of aggregate, and particularly the crushed rock aggregate, is an indication of the effect the particular source of aggregate has on the flexural strength.

This effect of the source of aggregate has several consequences for initial mix design procedure.

(1) If no previous data are available on the flexural strengths obtainable with the particular aggregate source, it is advisable to assume the lower line applicable to the gravel type of aggregate.

(2) In many instances, however, flexural strengths obtained will be considerably higher for any given value of compressive strength, and the mix design may require considerable modification before site work begins.

(3) Trial mixes are essential for concrete designed to meet a flexural strength specification. In view of the difficulties which might arise following point (2), the trials should be undertaken well in advance of site work.

(4) If the flexural strength required is above 7.5 N/mm² (1100 lbf/in²), it is no longer possible to assume that any crushed rock aggregate will be able to satisfy the requirements and it may prove necessary to haul more suitable aggregates over considerable distances. Clearly, where very high strengths are required, trial mixes must be started several months in advance of site work.

(5) It is possible that sources of material may be discovered which fall outside the indicated ranges.

A relation between indirect tensile and compressive strengths is given in Figure 6.2, which has been derived from the work of several investigators.[39, 51, 52] Again, one investigator [52] included concrete with and without entrained air; the air-entrained concrete had compressive strengths up to about 40 N/mm² (5800 lbf/in²). In designing for tensile strength, the effect of the type and source of aggregate is very similar to that found when designing for flexural strength and all the points (1) to (5) above apply. It will be seen that the indirect tensile strength is approximately two-thirds of the flexural strength.

6.3 Appearance

Whilst a high proportion of concrete is exposed to view and the need for a good appearance should always be recognized, there are many situations where a good appearance to the concrete becomes of paramount importance. Such terms as 'exposed concrete', 'decorative concrete', 'facing concrete', and even the deprecated term 'architectural concrete' have been used without exactly describing the intended meaning; perhaps they include all concrete in which a slight or even considerable increase in cost is acceptable in order to obtain a good appearance.

All that has already been said regarding the design of mixes applies to concrete of good appearance, though such work justifies emphasis on particular points depending upon the nature of the finish required. Perhaps the major

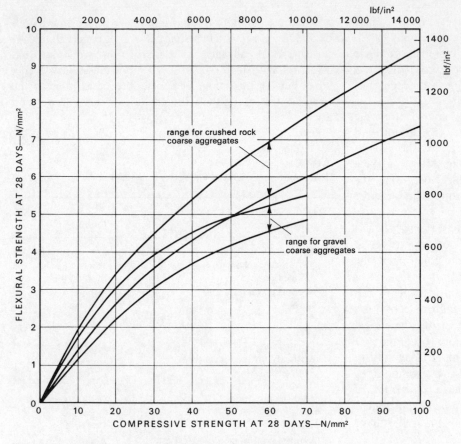

Figure 6.1 : Relation between flexural and compressive strength.

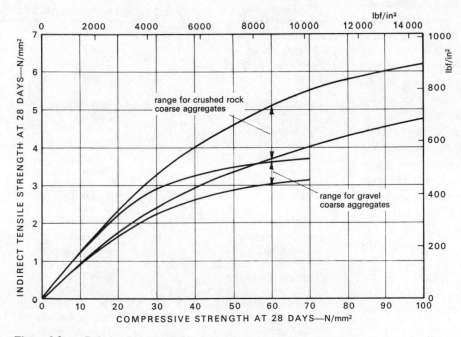

Figure 6.2 : Relation between indirect tensile and compressive strength.

point to be emphasized is that good appearance is in most instances synonymous with uniform appearance, and care is needed to ensure that all constituent materials, concrete manufacturing processes and casting procedures are controlled so as to provide the greatest degree of uniformity that is economically justified.

The colour of concrete is dependent on many factors: the colour of the cement and aggregates, the mix proportions, the nature of the forms and release agent, the rate of placing, the temperature and the curing. Many of these factors are beyond the scope of this book, but the constituent materials and their proportions require consideration.[53, 54]

The colour of cement is not a guaranteed property and it would be prohibitively expensive, if not impossible, to ensure that all cement was of uniform colour; but the frequent expedient of obtaining cement from one source or one works reduces variability to a considerable — and generally acceptable — extent. Far more uniform conditions can be obtained by using a coloured cement, where great care is taken to ensure uniformity of colour. If normal grey cement is being used, colour is much more likely to vary when the construction work extends over many months or years rather than weeks. Stocking large quantities of cement on site is not often a practicable possibility, particularly in view of the widespread use of ready mixed concrete.

Some aggregates are by their nature variable in colour, whereas others are remarkably uniform; particular sources are often chosen to influence and control the colour of concrete. Where the surface of the concrete is predominantly composed of cement paste the colour of the fine aggregate is important while that of the coarse aggregate is largely insignificant unless the concrete is liable to be worn or eroded during its working life. Where the aggregate is to be exposed — by grit-blasting, by using retarders on the formwork or by tooling the hardened surface — the colour of the coarse material becomes predominant. A list of coloured aggregates in the United Kingdom is given in Table 6.1, which is taken from a book by Wilson.[55] Information on the suppliers of these aggregates is constantly changing, but up-to-date names and addresses can be obtained from the Cement and Concrete Association.

Some impurities in aggregates which may mar the appearance of the concrete were discussed in Chapter 3.2.6. One point to note is that it may be impossible to ensure the complete absence of impurities. It is probable that if a few blemishes occur — for example, by the inclusion of the occasional particle of iron pyrites — this will have to be accepted on the grounds of overall economy and the particular spot will have to be made good.

Colouring pigments were discussed in Chapter 3.4.9. Whenever they are used, it is advisable to base acceptance of the mix proportions on the results of trial mixes because some pigments, such as carbon black, are liable to need a higher water/cement ratio to obtain adequate workability at any particular aggregate/cement ratio than a mix without the pigment. In practice this means that a slightly higher cement content may be necessary to maintain the required strength.

Where the concrete is required to have a particular colour or texture, it is most important that trial panels should be cast well in advance of construction work so that adjustments to materials or mix proportions can be made. When judging the colour of concrete to be exposed to the weather, the trial panels should be viewed both wet and dry.

TABLE 6.1
Some sources of coloured aggregates in the United Kingdom.

Name of quarry and petrological description	County
White	
'Permwhite' calcined flint	Essex
calcined flint	Staffordshire
Norwegian quartzite	imported
Marble	imported
Off-white	
Calcite spar	Derbyshire
Portland Capstone limestone	Dorsetshire
Ballidon limestone	Derbyshire
Dowlow limestone	Derbyshire
Abergele limestone	Denbighshire
Light grey	
Kimnay granite	Aberdeenshire
De Lank granite	Cornwall
Hingston Down granite	Cornwall
Goodygrane biotite granite	Cornwall
Norman E. May granite	Cornwall
Creetown biotite-granodiorite	Kirkcudbrightshire
Dark grey	
Burnside olivine basalt	Angus
Craighouse olivine basalt	Berwickshire
Penlee hornfels	Cornwall
Waterswallows olivine basalt	Derbyshire
Calton Hill basalt	Derbyshire
Dufton Moss quartz-dolerite	Durham
Easington Crag quartz-dolerite	Northumberland
Dunion:Jedburgh basalt	Roxburghshire
Clee Hill olivine dolerite	Shropshire
Black Rock hornfels	Westmorland
Blue Rock olivine basalt	Worcestershire
Whitwick	Leicestershire
Red/pink	
Corrennie granite	Aberdeenshire
Stoneycombe limestone	Devonshire
'Permmix' calcined flint	Essex
'Durite' calcined flint	Kent
Cloburn, Pettinain felsite	Lanarkshire
Mountsorrel soda granite	Leicestershire
Hardon red porphyrite	Northumberland
Shap granite	Westmorland
Purple/brown	
Moons Hill pyroxene-andesite	Somerset
Tuttle Hill quartzite	Warwickshire
Green	
Criggion olivine dolerite	Shropshire
Light blue	
Portishead slag, phosphorous slag	Somerset

The colour matching of one concrete to another is extremely difficult in practice. It is unwise to attempt to match adjacent sections of precast and in situ concrete — a deliberate contrast is usually preferable. One form of colour matching that is often necessary is in mortar used for filling bolt holes left by the formwork or for patching. The proportions of cement to fine aggregate in the mortar should be made the same as those of the main concrete, and the same fine aggregate should be used. However, because mortar will normally dry out to a rather darker colour than the mass of the concrete, the cement should be a mixture of about 75% of the type of cement used on the main concrete and about 25% of white Portland cement. Several trial samples should be made with different proportions of white cement and allowed to dry thoroughly before the best match is chosen. Where concrete is required to be of uniform colour and to have a dense surface of cement paste, it may be necessary to increase the minimum cement content beyond that which is required from durability and strength requirements. Recommended values are given in Table 6.2. [53, 54]

TABLE 6.2
Minimum cement contents for mixes to give good appearance.

Nominal maximum size of aggregate – mm (in.)	Minimum cement content of fully compacted concrete – kg/m³ (lb/yd³)
40 (1½)	330 (560)
20 (¾)	370 (620)
10 (3/8)	420 (710)

Most fresh concrete is liable to bleed, at least to a small extent, and it is advisable to design the mix to reduce this likelihood, which might otherwise lead to water runs or sand runs on vertical surfaces of the finished concrete. In general, excessive bleeding occurs with concrete of high workability having a coarse grading of fine aggregate and/or a low proportion of fine aggregate. A careful consideration of the proportions of fine aggregate at the trial mix stage is all that is generally required, though the use of a water-reducing admixture may prove beneficial.

Exposed aggregate concretes require the particle size and distribution of the coarse aggregate to be considered as well as the colour of the material. In general the best appearance is obtained by using as high a proportion of coarse aggregate in the surface as possible. This not only emphasizes the selected colour and texture of the aggregate but also helps reduce potential variation in the proportion of visible aggregate from one part of the surface to another. Large maximum sizes of aggregate also increase the proportion of the surface composed of aggregate. However, high proportions of coarse aggregate mean that the concrete is liable to be harsh and difficult to handle and place. To prevent segregation, the workability will have to relatively low; consequently, compaction must be by vibration and the rate of placing may have to be reduced. Coarse aggregates should be obtained in single sizes and batched separately in order to reduce variations in the proportions of large and small particles in the final surface.

The appearance of exposed aggregate concrete can often be further improved by using a gap-graded rather than a continuously graded aggregate. The coarse aggregate particles should be as uniform in size as is practicable and should be used in conjunction with as low a proportion of fine aggregate as is possible. The use of uniform-sized coarse aggregate particles has the advantage that the aggregate can be exposed to a greater extent, without dislodgement of particles, than is the case with continuously graded materials. Gap-graded concretes require very careful quality control and may entail particular problems regarding mixing, transporting and placing; for example, the satisfactory use of a concrete pump is unlikely.

6.4   Resistance to abrasion and slipperiness

The resistance of concrete to abrasion is largely related to the compressive strength of the concrete, at least so long as the abrasion is being withstood by the cement paste. Although few data exist concerning the strength needed to resist particular forms of abrasion, some suggested values are given in Table 6.3. Once the cement paste is worn away, an increasing proportion of the abrasive force is carried by the coarse aggregate. Soft sandstones and limestones are

TABLE 6.3
Concrete strength and resistance to abrasion.

Category	Application	Suggested lowest specified minimum or characteristic strength at 28 days – N/mm² (lbf/in²)
1	light pedestrian use (external)	25 (3600)
2	pneumatic-tyred and heavy pedestrian traffic	30 (4350)
3	marine structures subject to abrasion by sand or shingle; factory floors and paved areas frequently carrying tracked vehicles	40 (5800)

probably only suitable for category 1, whereas a wide range of aggregates would be suitable for categories 1 and 2 provided that the aggregate used in paving work does not wear so smooth as to become slippery. A crushed rock coarse aggregate of the basalt, granite or porphyry petrological groups, and some materials of the hornfels group, would be suitable for category 3.

Concrete can become slippery either when the cement paste and the coarse aggregate wear at the same rate, or when the cement paste wears away faster than the coarse aggregate and the coarse aggregate itself wears very smooth. In practice this means avoiding some, but not all, limestone and rounded flint gravel aggregates where slipperiness could present a hazard. Past experience of particular sources of aggregate is by far the best guide to potential slipperiness.

It should be noted that the skidding resistance of concrete, although partly dependent on the choice of constituent materials, is mainly dependent upon the surface texture to which the concrete is finished and is therefore beyond the scope of this book.

6.5 Air-entrained concrete

There are two circumstances in which it may be necessary to design an air-entrained concrete mix.[56] (This type of concrete was discussed in Chapter 3.4.6 with reference to the nature of the admixture, and in Chapter 5.7 with reference to its principal use, which is to offset the adverse effects of de-icing salt.) The first circumstance is when considerable data already exist regarding the properties of the cement and aggregates and regarding the mix proportions needed to provide the concrete with the required strength and workability without air entrainment; all that is needed is a relatively simple adjustment to the mix proportions of the plain concrete to meet the requirements of the air-entrained concrete. The second circumstance is when the air-entrained concrete mix has to be designed from first principles. It should be noted that it is not often possible to produce air-entrained concretes with a required average strength over about 45 to 50 N/mm^2 (about 7000 lbf/in^2) at 28 days. This is because higher-strength concretes generally have to have such low water contents that there is insufficient water to produce air bubbles efficiently.

The adjustment of mix proportions from a plain to an air-entrained concrete is relatively simple and the following procedure is sufficiently accurate for most purposes. Once it is accepted, firstly, that an air-entrained concrete will generally have a compressive strength about 10% lower than a plain mix of the same cement content and workability and, secondly, that air-entrained concretes tend to be rather more cohesive than plain mixes of similar cement content, workability and aggregate grading, then an arbitrary reduction in the aggregate content can be used to offset both factors at once. The quantity of aggregate per cubic metre (cubic yard) of concrete should be reduced by 30 kg (50lb); about two-thirds of this reduction should be taken off the fine aggregate and the rest off the coarse aggregate. This adjustment to the quantity of aggregate can then be

made to the batch quantities required for a trial mix; this should for preference be done under laboratory conditions, though full-scale site trials without benefit of laboratory mixes have proved perfectly successful. The making of trial mixes is discussed in Chapter 7, though the following additional points are relevant for air-entrained conrete.

The quantity of air-entraining admixture to be used in the trial mix should be calculated from the recommendations of the supplier of the admixture; typically it would be 0.05% by weight of cement. The admixture should be diluted in part of the mixing water and added to the solid constituents. Water should then be added until the workability is as required; initially this will have to be judged by eye, as the required amount of water will be somewhat lower than that used in the plain concrete of similar workability. Once the workability has been obtained and checked, the air content of the fresh concrete should be measured in a pressure-type air meter in accordance with BS 1881 : Part 2. The quantity of air may prove correct, or, perhaps more likely, it may be a little too high or too low compared with the values suggested in Chapter 3.4.6; this is because the correct dosage of admixture depends on many factors and the quantity initially suggested by the admixture supplier cannot be correct for all circumstances. If the dosage does prove incorrect, further trial mixes should be made using a greater or lesser dosage. Although it may be misleading to generalize, it usually appears worth while to change the dosage to a considerable extent, say 20 or 30%.

In general, the greater the quantity of admixture, the greater is the air content of the concrete; and the lower the workability, the greater the quantity of admixture required to give a particular air content. Thus, while small changes in workability and air content can be made by changing the amount of water and admixture respectively, both factors have to be changed when larger errors are to be corrected. For example, if the workability is correct but the air content is much too low, the quantity of admixture should be increased; but as this additional air will increase the workability, the quantity of water will probably have to be reduced for the second trial mix even though it has produced the correct workability in the first. The second trial mix will often prove to be successful but, if not, the third mix usually is. If necessary, slight changes in the proportion of fine aggregate can be made, though this should not be necessary.

When a mix of satisfactory air content and workability has been obtained, specimens should be cast for subsequent strength testing.

When little or no previous data exist regarding the constituent materials to be used or the mix proportions required, then a rather more complex mix design becomes necessary. The one suggested can be carried out using the data presented in Chapter 4.4, though with some modifications. The procedure is as follows.

(1) The target mean strength is estimated as in Chapter 4.2.

(2) This mean strength should be increased to allow for the slightly lower strength obtained with air-entrained concrete. The increase should be 20% for concretes of

aggregate/cement ratio about 4.5 by weight, 10% for those of aggregate/cement ratio about 6 by weight, whereas no allowance need be made for mixes as lean as 7.5 by weight. At this stage of the mix design the precise aggregate/cement ratio is not known, so a 10% value should generally be used unless experience suggests otherwise. Alternatively, a second run through this procedure can be made, up to (4) which is very quick.

(3) Using the value of compressive strength determined in (2), a water/cement ratio can be read from Figure 4.2.

(4) Using this water/cement ratio and knowing the type and maximum size of aggregate to be used, and having estimated the required workability, it is possible to determine the aggregate/cement ratio and type grading number from one of Tables 4.3 to 4.11 in the same way as suggested in Chapter 4.4.

(5) The proportion of cement to aggregate and the type grading just obtained can then be used in trial mixes, which should be treated in the same manner as has just been discussed. In particular, it should be noted that the quantity of water to be used is judged from the workability of the concrete; the quantity needed to obtain the required workability is likely to be less than that determined in (3) above.

The compressive strength test results obtained from trial mixes arrived at from either of the above procedures may prove unacceptably above or below the intended mean strength (1). The correction to the proportions can be estimated by working through Figure 4.2 and the appropriate table in the group 4.3 to 4.11. If the required change in strength is shown to be equivalent to a change in water/cement ratio of, say, 0.05, and to a change in aggregate/cement ratio of, say, 0.5, then the same numerical changes should be made to the mix proportions used in the trial mix. This principle of adjusting the mix proportions used in trial mixes to more nearly meet the required concrete proportions is discussed in general terms in Chapter 7.3.3.

If the above data have been obtained in the course of laboratory trial mixes, the full-scale site trials and construction work can probably start within a few days of the strength test results becoming available. The need for full-scale site trials arises because a given proportion of admixture will produce slightly different quantities of air, depending upon many factors including the size of the batch, the size and type of the mixer, and the mixing time. Thus the site trials are mainly to check the quantity of admixture required and to enable slight modifications to be made if necessary.

6.6 Accelerated and retarded stiffening times

6.6.1 Need to adjust the stiffening time of concrete

Conventional structural concrete made with ordinary Portland cement stiffens after mixing at a rate which is generally compatible with the rate at which the concrete is placed and compacted. Consequently there has been little incentive in the United Kingdom to investigate means of measuring or altering the normal rate of stiffening. The length of time for which concrete remains workable[57] varies from about one hour for concrete of high cement content and low workability to about four hours for concretes of low cement content and high workability. These figures, which relate to work at a temperature of 15 to 20°C, will also be affected by changes in temperature, to the extent of perhaps reducing the time to about three-quarters at 30°C and doubling the time at about 5°C.

There are, however, a few circumstances in the United Kingdom which justify the deliberate acceleration or retardation of the stiffening time of concrete. Examples of the need for acceleration are in sea defence work between tide levels, in cold-weather working and in emergency repair work. Examples of the need for retardation are slow placing conditions in hot weather and very large masses of concrete which take a considerable time to cast.

The fact that there is no generally accepted method of measuring the stiffening time of concrete is a disadvantage both to discussion of the subject and to the design of mixes for particular placing conditions. Where the subject proves important, the ASTM penetrometer test[58] should be used to assess comparatively a range of trial mixes of different proportions made with and without admixtures.

6.6.2 Accelerated stiffening

The only admixture frequently used to accelerate the rate of stiffening of concrete is calcium chloride, which also accelerates the rate of hardening (see Chapter 3.4.5). Typically, a dosage of calcium chloride of 1.5% anhydrous by weight of cement reduces the time of stiffening by about one hour at normal temperature and by rather more at higher temperatures; it is therefore generally considered advisable to place concrete containing calcium chloride within half an hour of the end of mixing during warm weather. Larger dosages of calcium chloride accelerate stiffening to a greater extent, but such dosages cannot be recommended for use in reinforced concrete because of the increased risk of corrosion of the steel.

6.6.3 Retarded stiffening

Retardation of stiffening can be brought about by using a cement of slower rate of reaction, such as a low heat Portland or low heat Portland blastfurnace cement, or by introducing a retarding admixture (see Chapters 3.1.6, 3.1.7 and 3.4.3). Due to the similarity between many retarders and water-reducing admixtures, Chapter 6.12 is also relevant.

6.7 Lightweight concrete [16, 17, 19]

6.7.1 General

In a large proportion of work the density of the concrete, typically 2300 kg/m³, is of no particular significance except as an indication of the extent of compaction of the concrete. Assuming that full compaction, adequate structural strength and good durability are obtained, further considerable benefits can be derived by using a concrete of lower density or, as it is usually called, a lightweight concrete. One major benefit is the reduced dead weight of a structure, which can reduce the size of the foundations and the costs of handling the concrete during construction. The other major benefit is the reduced coefficient of thermal conductivity of the lighter material which leads to improved thermal insulation; this latter aspect is discussed in some detail in Chapter 6.16.1.

Hardened concrete is composed essentially of silica, which has a specific gravity around 2.7, and other materials each having a specific gravity of a similar or higher value. A change in the basic materials is not often possible, and indeed any change that is possible will have relatively little benefit in terms of reducing the overall density. Reduced density is therefore brought about by introducing air into the concrete by one of a variety of means. These are summarized in Table 6.4, which deals with concretes that are likely to be used for structural purposes. (Lightweight concretes which are likely .to be used for non-structural purposes are discussed in Chapter 6.7.5). Aerated concretes are not discussed in detail, because such concretes are generally proprietary systems which would be appropriate for use in precast works where autoclaving techniques of curing can be used.

Mix design data have been prepared for several, though not all, proprietary lightweight aggregates available in the United Kingdom. In consequence it is necessary to rely to a greater extent than is normally necessary on the results of past work or trial mixes. In practice, trial mixes must be completed well in advance of the construction work and it is advisable, for example, to have data regarding compressive strength available for the age at which the strength is specified (generally 28 days), rather than to rely on the extrapolation of results of tests at an earlier age such as 7

days. Lightweight aggregates used in trial mixes should be in a similar moisture condition to those likely to be used on site, and allowance should be made, when adding water to the mix, for the moisture content of the aggregates.

6.7.2 Fully compacted lightweight aggregate concrete for structural purposes[18, 59, 60]

The specification of lightweight aggregate concretes will generally involve two factors in addition to those specified for dense aggregate concrete, namely the required density and the proprietary source of the type of aggregate to be used. Particular care needs to be taken regarding the condition of the concrete at which the density is measured. The value most convenient to specify is the density of the fresh concrete, as this can be measured quickly, and a standard test procedure has been laid down in BS 1881. This form of specification involves the specifying authority in judging the extent to which the concrete will dry out in the structure and thus its final density and thermal conductivity. If the specifying authority prefers to specify the air-dry density of the concrete, then the test procedure should also be specified; the final assessment of the trial mix results should, at least in theory, await the completion of drying tests which could take a considerable time. Specification of the required thermal conductivity of the concrete in the structure, without reference to density, is not thought practicable, at least for the time being.

The strength margin for lightweight aggregate concretes can be determined as described in Chapter 4.2. Workability should be judged in a rather different manner to that described in Chapter 4.3. The workability characteristics of lightweight aggregate concretes differ considerably from those of dense aggregate concretes; for example, a dense aggregate concrete of a particular compacting factor may be judged as suitable for one method of working, but this does

TABLE 6.4
Classification of lightweight concrete likely to be used for structural purposes.

Location of the air in the concrete	General description	Cross-reference
air contained in aggregate particles	fully compacted lightweight aggregate concrete	6.7.2
air contained between aggregate particles	no-fines dense aggregate concrete	6.7.3
	partially compacted dense aggregate concrete for blocks	6.21
		6.7.4
air contained both within and between aggregate particles	no-fines lightweight·aggregate concrete	
	partially compacted lightweight aggregate concrete for blocks	6.21
	air-entrained lightweight aggregate concrete	6.7.2
air or other gas contained in cement mortar	aerated concrete	see references 16 and 17

not mean that the most appropriate value of compacting factor for the lightweight aggregate concrete is necessarily the same. The most appropriate workability must therefore be judged largely from previous experience or from trials using the method of compaction intended for the full-scale work. As the specific gravity of the lightweight aggregate may be substantially lower than that of the cement mortar, prolonged vibration should be avoided as this can cause the aggregate particles to float to the surface. Lightweight aggregate concrete will generally have a good workability if the compacting factor exceeds 0.8 or if the Vebe time is less than 12 seconds. An examination of the properties of lightweight aggregate concrete shows that, for a particular aggregate, the compacting factor is closely related to the total water content of the mix. Use is made of this relation in the following mix design procedure, which is taken from work by Teychenné[18]

(1) Using Figure 6.3, the required average total water/cement ratio with ordinary Portland cement is determined from the required average strength. This may show that some proprietary materials are unlikely to be suitable for the work.

(2) The required workability is selected from Table 6.5 and the corresponding total water content is used in Figure 6.3 to give the required cement content.

TABLE 6.5
Required total water content in fresh lightweight aggregate concrete for different degrees of workability.

Workability	Name of proprietary aggregate	Approximate total water content – kg/m³ (lb/yd³)
medium	Aglite	310 (520)
	foamed slag	380 (640)
	Leca	260 (440)
	Lytag	340 (570)
low	Aglite	250 (420)
	foamed slag	340 (570)
	Leca	240 (400)
	Lytag	280 (470)

(3) From a knowledge of the type of aggregate and the required cement content, the likely range of fresh and air-dried density can be estimated to within about 50 kg/m³ (3 lbf/ft³) from Figure 6.3. If the density for a particular material does not meet the specification requirement, then that material is likely to be unsuitable and another must be selected.

(4) All values should be carefully checked against comprehensive previous data or by means of trial mixes. To calculate the mix proportions per cubic metre (cubic yard) of fully compacted fresh concrete, the cement content and water content, which are known, are both taken from the density of the fresh concrete to give the total weight of dry aggregate.

The proportion of fine to total aggregate, which is generally in the range 40 to 50%, should also be judged at the trial mix stage. In the absence of any previous data a value of

45% could be accepted for the first trials. The manufacturers of the aggregate can usually give guidance on this and other points.

Lightweight coarse aggregates can be, and often are, used in conjunction with natural dense fine aggregates. It is however, not practicable on the basis of present data to suggest a general mix design procedure which would be applicable to several proprietary materials. In general, higher strengths and higher densities will be obtained using natural fine aggregate, and the extent of such changes depends on the proportion of fine to total aggregate. Trial mixes should therefore be made with proportions judged as suitable from previous work with the particular lightweight aggregate. One point to note is that the specific gravities of the coarse and fine aggregates differ considerably, and any calculation of the proportion of fine aggregate on a weight basis will have to take this difference into account. For example, if past experience of factors such as those discussed in Chapter 4.4.2 suggests that a fine aggregate proportion of 40% is appropriate for use in a trial mix, and the apparent specific gravities of the fine and coarse aggregate are 2.65 and 1.6 respectively, then the proportions by weight of fine and coarse aggregate to batch are 24 (ie, 40 x 1.6/2.65) and 60 respectively.

Air entrainment is frequently used in lightweight aggregate concrete, partly because its inclusion reduces the density of the concrete and improves its thermal properties, and partly to improve the handling characteristics of the fresh concrete. Lightweight fine aggregates are often crushed materials and they tend to produce a concrete which is harsh and liable to bleed; although an increase in the proportion of fine material can improve these properties, it is often found that a better result is obtained by using air entrainment. To date, little mix design data are available for lightweight aggregate concretes containing entrained air. Information on Solite indicates that the inclusion of about 5% of entrained air enables the water content to be reduced by about 20 kg/m³ (34 lb/yd³) and that there is a considerable improvement in the relation between density and the strength of the concrete; higher air contents up to about 10% and the inclusion of water-reducing admixtures can have further benefits.

The air content of lightweight aggregate concrete is generally measured by a gravimetric method since the pressure method clearly gives erroneous results. Some care is needed, however, in the calculation of results since the water contents of the plain and air-entrained concretes are likely to be different.

6.7.3 No-fines dense aggregate concrete

No-fines dense aggregate concrete would normally have a minimum or characteristic compressive strength of 3 N/mm² (435 lbf/in²) at 28 days when tested in accordance with BS 1881. The materials used would generally be ordinary Portland cement and a single-sized coarse aggregate complying with BS 882. The aggregate would be nominally graded from 40 − 20 mm (1½ − ¾ in.), or 20 −

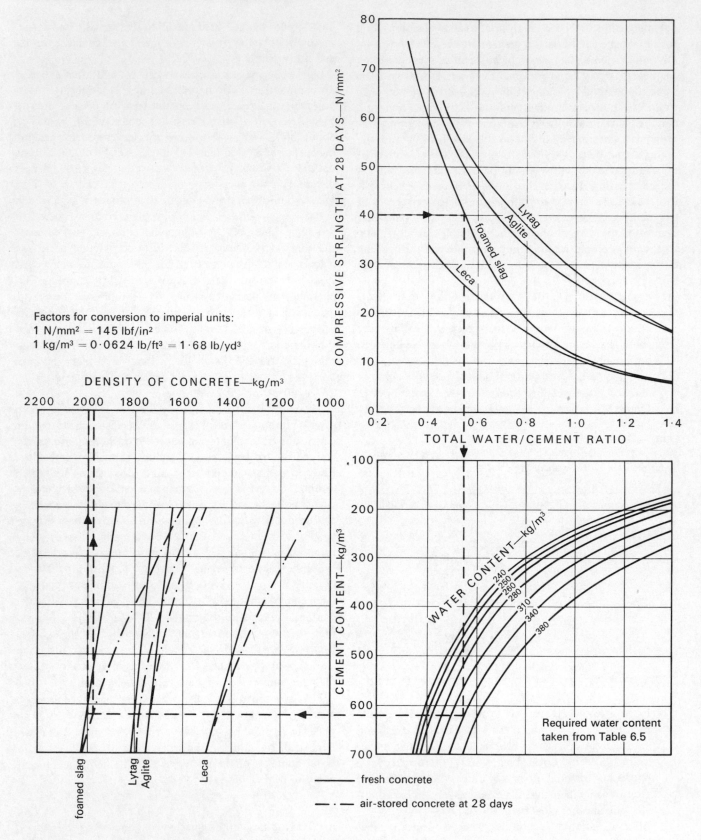

Factors for conversion to imperial units:
1 N/mm² = 145 lbf/in²
1 kg/m³ = 0·0624 lb/ft³ = 1·68 lb/yd³

Figure 6.3 : Mix design for lightweight-aggregate concrete [18].

Example. The broken line shows that a mix containing foamed slag, designed to have a low workability and a 28-day compressive strength of 40 N/mm², will have a total water/cement ratio of 0.55, a cement content of 625 kg/m³ (the water content figure being taken from Table 6.5) and wet and dry densities of about 2000 and 1970 kg/m³ respectively.

10 mm (3/4 – 3/8 in.), or 10 – 5 mm (3/8 – 3/16 in.). Whichever size is used, the proportions of over-sized and under-sized materials must be kept as low as possible; generally, not more than 10% by weight over-size or 5% under-size should be used. If the range of aggregate particle sizes is too great, this will result in a lower voids content in the compacted concrete which, of course, nullifies one of the primary objects in making no-fines concrete.

The proportions of cement : aggregate : water should be selected so that the aggregate particles in the fresh concrete are coated with a layer of cement-and-water paste; the paste should adhere to the aggregate, and the coated coarse aggregate particles should make point-to-point contact to ensure bonding of the particles sufficient to meet the compressive strength requirements without the interstices between the aggregate particles being blocked with cement paste. The most appropriate proportions should be determined partly on a basis of experience and partly on the compressive strength, when this has been measured following the making of trial mixes. Some experience is necessary because incorrect judgement of the water/cement ratio can easily result in the paste being too dry to coat the aggregate particles fully, or so wet that it flows off them.

As the water/cement ratio is limited to an optimum value between these extreme conditions, and the cement content cannot be varied widely without either the particles being inadequately covered or the interstices becoming over-filled, there is in effect only one 'best mix' for any size and source of aggregate. Consequently there is not much freedom to vary the strength of such concretes. Minimum strengths higher than 3 N/mm^2 (435 lbf/in^2) at 28 days can be specified, but the greater cement contents required could result in a filling of the interstices, espcially for minimum strengths greater than about 6 N/mm^2 (870 lbf/in^2).

It is important to make trial mixes to check strength, because a slight change in the extent to which the interstices are filled, due either to an excess of cement or to an excess of over-sized or under-sized particles, will have a significant effect on the compressive strength. It should be noted that no-fines concrete is compacted by hand tamping and not by vibration. It is suggested that three trial mixes

should be made when deciding the most appropriate aggregate/cement ratio to use with any particular source and size of aggregate. It may be possible to discard one or more of the mixes from the appearance of the concrete. Lower aggregate/cement ratios would generally be appropriate for smaller-size aggregates and for aggregates of poor particle shape. Suitable aggregate/cement ratios by bulk volume would be 9, 10 and 11 for 40 mm (1½ in.) aggregate, 8, 9 and 10 for 20 mm (¾ in.) aggregate and 7, 8 and 9 for 10 mm (3/8 in.) aggregate.

6.7.4 No-fines lightweight aggregate concrete

No-fines lightweight aggregate concrete is similar in many respects to no-fines concrete made with dense aggregate. There is often not such a wide range of aggregate sizes available, though the aggregate may be of more uniform particle size and may be more rounded. The effect of this is that the cement contents are often rather less than with dense aggregate, and the strength is generally lower.

6.7.5 Lightweight aggregate concrete for non-structural purposes

The lightest of lightweight aggregates are not suitable for structural work and would normally be used for insulation only. The most appropriate mix proportions depend on the nature of the material and the method of using the concrete; guidance on suitable values can generally be obtained from the suppliers of the aggregates. Some typical figures[16] are given in Table 6.6, which includes values for drying shrinkage; this is liable to be relatively high for this type of concrete as compared with conventional dense aggregate concrete.

6.8 High-density concrete

The term 'high-density concrete' can mean that the concrete has merely been compacted to the greatest possible extent and that virtually all the air, the lightest component, has been excluded. An alternative and probably more important meaning is that the density of the

TABLE 6.6
Typical properties of insulating lightweight aggregate concrete.

Aggregate type	Aggregate/cement ratio by bulk volume	Air-dry density –kg/m^3 (lb/ft^3)	Minimum compressive strength at 28 days – N/mm^2 (lbf/in^2)	Thermal conductivity –W/m°C (Btu in/ft^2 h °F)	Drying shrinkage – %
vermiculite	8	400 (25)	0.7 (100)	0.09 to 0.16	
	6	480 (30)	1.0 (135)	(0.6 to 1.1)	0.35 to 0.45
	4	560 (35)	1.2 (175)		
perlite	7	400 (25)	1.4 (200)	0.10 to 0.17	
	6	480 (30)	2.2 (310)	(0.7 to 1.2)	0.14 to 0.20
	5	560 (35)	3.4 (490)		
	4	640 (40)	4.8 (690)		
graded wood particles	4	640 (40)	1.8 (250)	0.20 to 0.29	
	3	880 (55)	4.9 (700)	(1.4 to 2.0)	0.25 to 0.50
	2	1200 (75)	12.2 (1750)		

fully compacted concrete is made significantly higher than normal, generally so that the concrete may have greater resistance to penetration by X-rays or gamma rays.

Apart from entrapped air, the component of lowest density in concrete is the cement paste which has a specific gravity between about 1.7 and 2.1, depending upon the water/cement ratio; the specific gravity of cement is about 3.1. Since all natural aggregates in the United Kingdom have significantly higher specific gravities than the cement paste, it follows that, assuming full compaction, the greatest densities are obtained using mixes of as low a water/cement ratio and as high an aggregate/cement ratio as possible. Therefore, so far as is practicable, large maximum sizes of aggregate and low workabilities should be used.

The specific gravities of natural concreting aggregates in the United Kingdom vary from about 2.5 to about 3.0, with the flint gravels and quartzites generally in the lower half of the range and the hornfels, granite and basalt groups of rocks generally in the upper half.

Taking as a basis for comparison a concrete mix of cement content 300 kg/m^3 (510 lb/yd^3) and water/cement ratio 0.6, wet concrete densities in the range 2300 – 2650 kg/m^3 (145 – 165 lb/ft^3) and dry concrete densities in the range 2175 – 2530 kg/m^3 (135 – 158 lb/ft^3) can be obtained with these aggregates. Higher densities can be obtained by using other aggregates such as barytes, steel shot, sheet punchings or lead shot. Typical densities obtained with these materials are given in Table 6.7. To check the actual densities obtained using particular materials and mix proportions it is necessary to make trial mixes and measure the density of the fresh concrete and then to allow for loss of water on drying. It can generally be assumed that one-third of the free water/cement ratio is taken up in hydration and that two-thirds will ultimately evaporate.

In making concrete of high density, it will be found that the constituents are more likely to segregate than they are with concretes made with normal-density aggregates. This is due to the very considerably greater difference in the specific gravity between the mortar or cement paste and the coarse aggregate. In practice this means that concretes of relatively low workability will have to be used. The normal methods of measuring workability are also misleading, and the most appropriate workabililty will have to be judged from the ease with which the concrete can be compacted into test specimens or into a simulated trial section of the work.

Concrete made with barytes aggregate may not gain strength with age in the same manner as is generally the case with more conventional materials. For example, with a 20 mm (¾ in.) maximum size of aggregate it may not be easy to obtain strengths exceeding 45 N/mm^2 (6500 lbf/in^2) with a cement content around 500 kg/m^3 (840 lb/yd^3), nor 22 N/mm^2 (3200lbf/in^2) with a cement content around 300 kg/m^3 (510 lb/yd^3). The making of trial mixes is therefore essential if an accurate mix is to be achieved. Fortunately the possible limitations on strength are not likely to present a difficult problem because such concretes are generally used in fairly thick sections where high stresses are not likely to be developed.

6.9 Low heat of hydration

One of the basic properties of cement is that heat is evolved during the process of chemical hydration, the amount of which is in effect a measure of the reactivity of the cement. The heat evolved can be an advantage in helping to maintain newly placed concrete above freezing point during winter building, or it can be a disadvantage in hot weather when concrete is cast in large masses – high peak temperatures can be reached in the first few days after casting, and cracking of the concrete can occur on subsequent cooling. The extent of temperature rise and the possibility of cracking can justify special consideration being given to the design of concrete mixes to reduce these effects.

Fundamental to this aim is the fact that the strength of concrete is also a measure of the reactivity of cement and is therefore approximately related to the heat development; therefore mixes designed to reach a certain strength will develop approximately the same heat of hydration whether a cement with low heat of hydration characteristics is used in relatively large proportions or a more rapid-hardening cement is used in a smaller proportion. However, if a high proportion of the heat developed can be dissipated before the age at which the concrete strength is specified, advantage can be taken of using low heat cements; in practice this

TABLE 6.7
High-density aggregates and concretes.

Type of aggregate	Approximate specific gravity of heavy aggregate	Approximate density of fresh concrete – kg/m^3 (lb/ft^3)
bartyes coarse (with normal-density fine aggregate)	4.0	3000 (190)
barytes coarse and fine	4.0	3300 (205)
steel punchings or shot (with normal-density fine aggregate)	7.8	4800 (300)
lead shot (with normal-density fine aggregate)	11.4	7000 (440)

means that strength specifications should refer to an age of at least 28 days and probably later.

Other means of reducing the rate or amount of heat evolved include the use of water-reducing and retarding admixtures (discussed in Chapters 3.4.4 and 6.12), the partial replacement of cement by pulverized-fuel ash (discussed in Chapters 3.4.8 and 6.11), and the use of very large aggregate sizes of 75 mm (3 in.) to 150 mm (6 in.) (discussed in Chapter 6.10). It is not unusual to employ all three of these expedients and to use a low heat Portland cement in very large masses of concrete, such as in dams, where an excessive build-up of heat is likely to lead to cracking. These techniques can sometimes also be justified as a means of reducing the cost of concrete.

6.10 Large maximum-size aggregate [61]

6.10.1 Selection of constituent materials

The use of large maximum sizes of aggregate, between 75 mm (3 in.) and 150 mm (6 in.), generally enables the cement content of the concrete to be reduced very considerably as compared with the more conventional maximum sizes of 20 mm (¾ in.) and 40 mm (1½ in.), whilst the concrete maintains comparable strength and workability.

The maximum size of the aggregate selected for very large sections of mass concrete work will depend upon a number of factors and will generally fall between 75 mm (3 in.) and 150 mm (6 in.). Even larger maximum sizes can be used, but are liable to result in excessive wear in batching and mixing plants, leading to high plant maintenance costs; smaller sizes do not realize as great a reduction in cement content as is reasonably possible.

The situations in which work of this type is being undertaken are generally very large one-off jobs far away from developed areas, with the result that aggregates have to be located and specially prepared for use. Local deposits have therefore to be examined very carefully, for it is likely that the cost of the aggregate and its preparation will form a substantial proportion of the cost of the work. In the United Kingdom it is likely that the aggregate will be a crushed rock because there are few deposits of large-size gravel available.

Aggregate preparation plant will have to be set up. One of the objectives, when selecting plant, will be to obtain a grading and particle shape of aggregate suitable for the production of concrete. Moreover, it is uneconomic to discard large quantities of unwanted sizes of aggregate; this applies particularly to crushed rock flour which would pass a 75 μm (No. 200) test sieve and is liable to be produced in large quantities.

It is not possible to generalize on the most appropriate type of crushing plant to use, partly because the nature of the rock influences the choice; three points should, however, be noted.
(1) The extent to which the rock is crushed by any one crusher should be limited because high crushing ratios are liable to lead to the production of aggregate of poor particle shape and a high proportion of flour. Therefore it might be found more economic, for example, to crush large lumps of rock progressively in three crushers with a low crushing ratio rather than to use only two crushers and get an aggregate which requires a higher cement content in the concrete.
(2) Lean concretes having a large maximum size aggregate are more liable to segregate than concretes of smaller maximum size, and there is a relatively small range of water content within which segregation can be controlled. It is therefore important that the grading of aggregate does not vary too much from one batch of concrete to the next. Probably the most effective way of avoiding excessive variation is to split the coarse aggregate into a number of single sizes and to batch the sizes separately. This may need a considerable amount of screening plant and storage space for the aggregate and can complicate the batching plant and procedure. In practice, however, quite extensive aggregate preparation plant often proves justified.
(3) The tendency for lean concretes to segregate has sometimes to be offset by incorporating some of the crushed rock flour or other materials, which improves the cohesiveness. Among these materials are natural sand of fine grading (say, zone 4 of BS 882), water-reducing admixtures, air-entraining admixtures and pulverized-fuel ash. Air-entraining admixtures have the further advantage of improving the durability of the concrete against freezing and thawing and may result in an improvement in the strength of the concrete (see Chapter 6.5).

Whatever materials are selected, experience shows that considerable care must be taken to ensure that good control is maintained over the quality.

6.10.2 Mix proportions

Past experience shows that the aggregate grading should, so far as possible, fall within the envelopes given in Figures 6.4 and 6.5 for aggregates of 75 mm (3 in.) and 150 mm (6 in.) maximum sizes respectively. The percentage of fine aggregate by weight of total aggregate has often been in the range 27 to 33 for 75 mm (3 in.) aggregate and 23 to 27 for 150 mm (6 in.) aggregate, with a tendency for air-entrained concretes to require less fine aggregate. The grading of the fine aggregate generally approximates to zone 2 of BS 882.

The water/cement ratios used are generally in the range 0.5 to 0.7. The aggregate/cement ratios are generally in the range 6 to 9 by weight for 75 mm (3 in.) aggregate and 8 to 15 by weight for 150 mm (6 in.) aggregate.

Although it is usual to specify that concretes having a large maximum size of aggregate should attain a particular minimum strength, the testing of such concretes presents a problem because, ideally, very large test specimens and test apparatus would have to be used. Large specimens and apparatus have been used, but the preferable procedure is to specify that the freshly sampled concrete should be screened on a 37.5 mm (1½ in.) sieve and the material passing should then be subject to testing in accordance

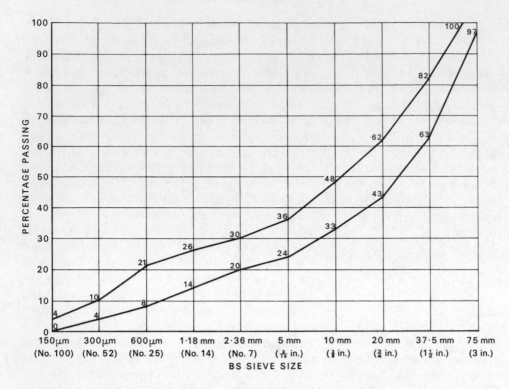

Figure 6.4 : Grading envelope for 75 mm (3 in.) maximum-size aggregate.

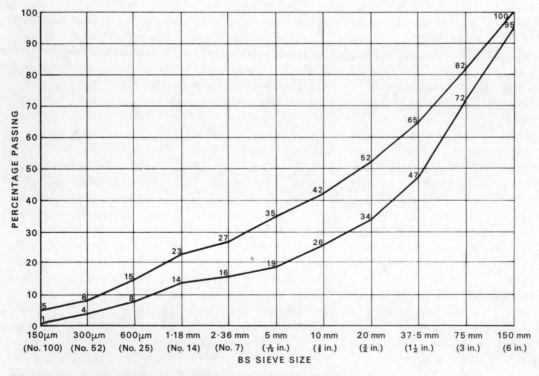

Figure 6.5 : Grading envelope for 150 mm (6 in.) maximum-size aggregate.

with BS 1881. In this way the concrete can be tested for workability, strength and air content for the purpose of checking both compliance and quality control. If screened samples of concrete are used, the relation between compressive strength and water/cement ratio given in Figure 4.2 can be used for ordinary Portland cement.

It is essential that full-scale trial mixes should be made well in advance of construction work, because any preliminary mix design and the results of any laboratory trial mixes are only approximate and must be verified under full working conditions.

6.11 Pulverized-fuel ash

No completely satisfactory mix design technique has yet been developed for concretes containing pulverized-fuel ash (pfa). This is largely because of the wide range of ashes currently available and the wide range of cements and aggregates with which the ash might be incorporated. There are, however, two measurements of the properties of pfa which should be considered. The first is a knowledge of the amount of water needed to wet the surface of the particles of ash; this can be assessed by carrying out a standard consistence test for the ash as though it were cement being tested in accordance with BS 12.

Provided the amount of water needed with the ash is not greater than the amount needed with the cement with which the ash is to be used, then the inclusion of the ash in the concrete is not likely to require an excessive addition of water to make the concrete workable.

The second fact required about the ash is a knowledge of its cementing efficiency, K. The cementing efficiency of an ash is that quantity of cement which has an equivalent effect on the strength of a concrete mix as would a unit weight of ash. A numerical value of 0.25 is sometimes suggested, though the actual value varies with the source of the ash and the age at which the strength of the concrete is being considered.

Even though these two properties of pulverized-fuel ash can be identified and to some extent related to the properties which they impart to a concrete mix, they cannot yet be used satisfactorily in the systematic design of a mix; considerable reliance still has to be placed on trial and error. Probably one of the best starting points is the data in Table 6.8, which have been reproduced with minor editiorial changes from reference 32. This table relates the weights of cement, aggregate, ash and water in a unit volume of fully compacted concrete to the workability and compressive strength. Three types of 20 mm maximum-size aggregate are considered; the water requirement of the ash is the same as that of the cement, and the K value is 0.25. Data are given for three levels of target mean 28-day strength, 16.7, 37.5 and 52.5 N/mm² (2400, 5450 and 7600 lbf/in²), which would correspond to minimum or characteristic strengths of 12.5, 30 and 45 N/mm² (1800, 4350 and 6500 lbf/in²) when very good quality control is attained during production, or to rather lower strengths of 10, 22.5 and 37.5 N/mm² (1450, 3250 and 5450 lbf/in²) when the quality control is not proven or is

known to be poor. Thus, when working from a job specification in which the minimum or characteristic strength is given, some interpolation may be necessary, using the weights of materials in the appropriate column to the right of the table.

Now, to take an example, suppose a target mean strength of 37.5 N/mm² is thought appropriate and it is intended to use an irregular gravel aggregate and a 'medium' workability. First, a trial mix based on the proportions of 180 : 290 : 160 : 1760 of water : cement : ash : aggregate (with an appropriate breakdown of the weight of aggregate into coarse and fine aggregate) is made. One of the first factors to be noted and measured is the workability of the concrete, which may be higher, lower or as intended; if it is higher, the most likely explanation is either that the water requirement of the ash is lower than that of the cement or that the particular irregular aggregate has a better particle shape, surface texture or grading than that used for compiling the table; conversely, a lower workability could mean the ash has a higher water requirement than the cement or that the aggregate properties are less favourable than when the table was compiled; if the workability is as intended, it may be possible that the two factors just mentioned are both operating but in opposite directions. Nevertheless, assuming the workability is not quite as intended, a second trial mix should be made in which the amount of water is adjusted to get closer to the required workability; a change in compacting factor of 0.02 is the equivalent of about 5 kg/m³ of water. Now, assuming the correct workability has been obtained, test cubes will be cast; however, the so far unproven K factor of the ash and the change in water content to correct the workability will affect the compressive strength of the concrete, so it would be wise to make two further trial mixes at once to ensure, so far as is reasonably possible, that the strengths of the mixes made will cover the target value.

In the first two trial mixes discussed, the proportion of cement to ash was 290 160. Now, keeping in mind that the specific gravity of the ash is about 2.1 against 3.15 for cement, the proportions of the two should be changed in such a way that the total volume of the particles of cement and ash should remain sensibly the same. That is, to cover a reasonably wide range of proportions of cement to ash, two trial mixes should be made, in which the quantity of cement is increased and then decreased by 15% while the quantity of ash is decreased and then increased by 10% to give two mixes in which the proportions of cement to ash are 334 : 144 and 246 : 176.

There remains one further possibility, that there may in these particular circumstances be no advantage in using pulverized-fuel ash at all; therefore, yet another trial mix should be designed, made and tested without the ash, as is discussed elsewhere in this book.

When the strength test results are available, there will be results for three mixes containing ash from which it should be possible to interpolate the mix proportions to meet more closely the target strength, and a further result for the mix without ash. The final choice for the construction work would then be between the interpolated ash mix and the mix without ash; the governing factor would be the

TABLE 6.8 (metric units)
Suggested trial mix proportions for particular compressive strengths.

Target mean compressive strength – N/mm²			Weights of materials in kg/m³ required in fully compacted concrete using 20 mm maximum size aggregate (all weights to nearest 10 kg)								
7 days	28 days		Rounded gravel			Irregular gravel			Crushed rock		
		Workability	Low	Medium	High	Low	Medium	High	Low	Medium	High
		Slump – mm	13-25	25-51	51-127	13-25	25-51	51-127	13-25	25-51	51-127
		Compacting factor	0.85	0.92	0.95	0.85	0.92	0.95	0.85	0.92	0.95
11.2	16.7	water	150	170	180	170	180	200	200	210	220
		OPC	120	140	150	140	150	160	160	170	180
		pfa	200	230	240	230	250	260	260	290	300
		aggregate	1910	1860	1820	1860	1790	1770	1770	1720	1690
30.0	37.5	water	140	170	180	170	180	180	180	200	210
		OPC	230	260	270	260	290	300	300	320	330
		pfa	120	140	150	140	160	170	170	180	190
		aggregate	1890	1820	1790	1820	1760	1730	1730	1680	1650
41.0	52.5	water				170			180	180	
		OPC	*	*	*	430	*	*	390	440	*
		pfa				20			70	60	
		aggregate				1760			1750	1690	

*Mixes not sutiable for pfa.

TABLE 6.8 (imperial units)
Suggested trial mix proportions for particular compressive strengths.

Target mean compressive strength – lbf/in²			Weights of materials in lb/yd³ required in fully compacted concrete using ¾ in. maximum size aggregate (all weights to nearest 10 lb)								
7 days	28 days		Rounded gravel			Irregular gravel			Crushed rock		
		Workability	Low	Medium	High	Low	Medium	High	Low	Medium	High
		Slump – in.	½-1	1-2	2-5	½-1	1-2	2-5	½-1	1-2	2-5
		Compacting factor	0.85	0.92	0.95	0.85	0.92	0.95	0.85	0.92	0.95
1625	2400	water	250	280	300	280	290	330	330	350	370
		OPC	200	230	250	230	260	270	270	290	310
		pfa	330	380	400	380	420	440	440	480	500
		aggregate	3220	3130	3060	3130	3010	2980	2980	2900	2840
4350	5450	water	240	280	290	280	310	310	310	340	360
		OPC	380	430	460	430	480	500	500	540	560
		pfa	210	240	260	240	270	280	280	300	320
		aggregate	3180	3060	3010	3060	2960	2910	2910	2830	2770
5950	7600	water				280			290	310	
		OPC	*	*	*	730	*	*	650	740	*
		pfa				40			120	100	
		aggregate				2960			2950	2850	

*Mixes not suitable for pfa.

relative cost of the two mixes, not forgetting the extra cost involved on site in handling, storing and batching the extra ingredient.

6.12 Water-reducing admixtures

As discussed in Chapter 3.4.2, water-reducing admixtures can prove beneficial to concrete in several applications. The design of a mix to include a water-reducing admixture must therefore depend to some extent upon the objective in using it. Further, as previously noted, there are many proprietary materials, each with slightly different properties, and the effectiveness of the materials depends upon the properties of the cement with which it is to be used. Inevitably, therefore, the choice of whether or not to use the admixture must be upon the basis of comparing the results of trial mixes with and without the admixture, and the mix proportions finally used must be determined largely by trial and error.

In general, the comparative mix without the admixture should be designed or determined from previous data to meet the requirements in the normal way. The trial mix should be made using the same sources of cement and aggregate as will be

Depending on the objective in using the admixture, the following should also be done at the same time.

(1) If the objective in using the admixture is to improve the workability of the concrete, a further trial mix should be made incorporating the quantity of admixture recommended by the suppliers; this trial mix should have the same proportions of cement, aggregate and water as the plain mix, though the proportions of fine to coarse aggregate may require adjustment for the best results. Although a comparison of slump and perhaps compacting factor and Vebe results will be made, the general handlability and compactability should also be judged because the normal methods of measuring workability do not reflect all its aspects. Test specimens should be cast and tested to ensure the concrete will have adequate strength when hardened. If the concrete with the admixture has a significantly different strength from that without it, this difference should be taken into account, together with the workability, when assessing the overall benefit of the admixture and whether or not its cost is justified.

(2) If the objective in using the admixture is to reduce the quantity of water in the mix and consequently to increase the strength, the water content of the trial mix containing the admixture will have to be judged by eye to match as closely as possible the workability of the plain mix; this may involve more than one trial mix with the admixture. Comparative strength test results will then show the effectiveness of the admixture.

(3) If the objective is to reduce the cement content of the concrete, the first point to decide is how much of a reduction in cement content would justify the use of the admixture — a figure of 10% might be appropriate. The trial mix containing the admixture should then have a cement content 10% less than the plain concrete and the amount of water added to this mix should be judged to give the same workability as the plain concrete. Again, more than one trial mix may have to be made. The strength of the plain and admixture concretes should then be compared in the normal way to arrive at a decision as to whether the admixture is sufficiently effective to be economically justified. A point to note is that if the admixture is to prove effective it is likely that the water/cement ratios of the mixes will be reasonably similar.

6.13 Low drying shrinkage

Concrete undergoes drying shrinkage when it dries out, and some assessment of the likely movement is often required when a structure is being designed. A large number of factors affect the amount of drying shrinkage, including the nature of the constituent materials, the mix proportions, the environment in which the concrete is drying, the size of the concrete member or specimen being considered, the duration of drying, and whether or not the concrete contains reinforcing steel. Some allowance can be made for these factors, but such allowances are only approximate.

The position is further complicated by the wide variety of test methods which have been used to measure drying shrinkage; since these methods are known to affect the results, it is not often possible to relate the work of one investigation to that of another. One of the most comprehensive methods of estimating the drying shrinkage of a concrete member is that of the joint CEB-FIP Recommendations.[7] These apply to Portland cement concrete containing dense natural aggregate, and take account of the relative humidity at which the concrete is maintained, the cement content, the water/cement ratio, the cross-sectional area of the member divided by half the perimeter exposed to the atmosphere, the time and the proportion of reinforcing steel in the concrete. If the allowance for reinforcing steel is omitted, the drying shrinkage is the product of the ordinates of the four graphs given in Figures 6.6 to 6.9. Even though the final estimate of drying shrinkage can be questioned because other variables are not considered, the relative importance of the factors included can at least be estimated and the concrete mix proportions judged accordingly.

The effect of cement content and water/cement ratio, shown in Figure 6.7, can very largely be replaced by a simpler relation showing that it is the water content of the concrete which is mainly responsible for changes in drying shrinkage and that, where a low drying shrinkage is required, the concrete mix should be designed for as low a water content as possible. Since water content is approximately related to workability for any particular type of aggregate, the aim, when drying shrinkage has to be kept to a minimum, becomes one of using as large a maximum size of aggregate, as low a proportion of fine aggregate and as low a workability of concrete as possible.

Air entrainment does not appear to affect either the rate or the total amount of drying shrinkage in normal conditions.[62]

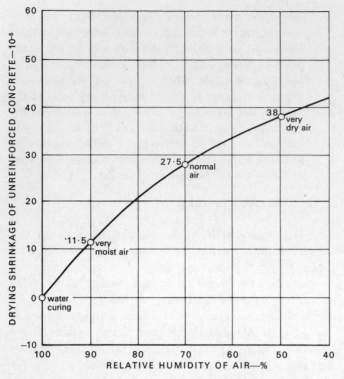

Figure 6.6 : Relation between drying shrinkage of unreinforced concrete and relative humidity.

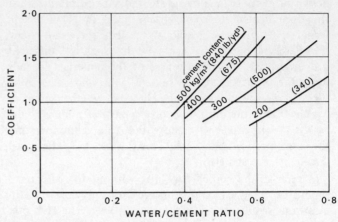

Figure 6.7 : Coefficient for composition of concrete.

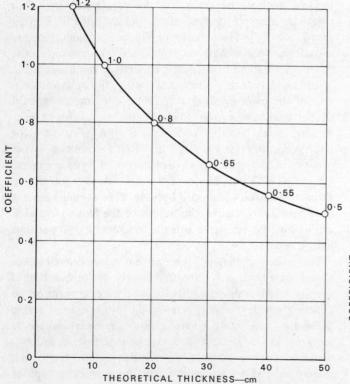

Figure 6.8 : Drying shrinkage coefficient for the size of a concrete member. (The theoretical thickness is the quotient of the area of the section divided by half the perimeter in contact with the atmosphere.)

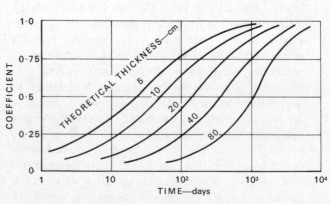

Figure 6.9 : Coefficient for time.

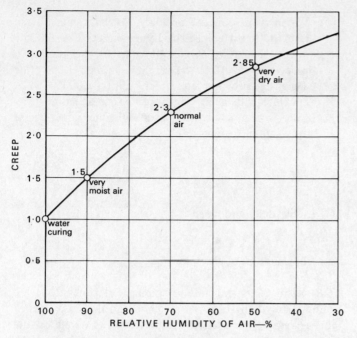

Figure 6.10 : Relation between creep (as a proportion of initial elastic strain) and relative humidity.

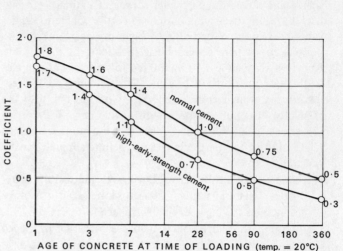

Figure 6.11 : Coefficient for time of loading.

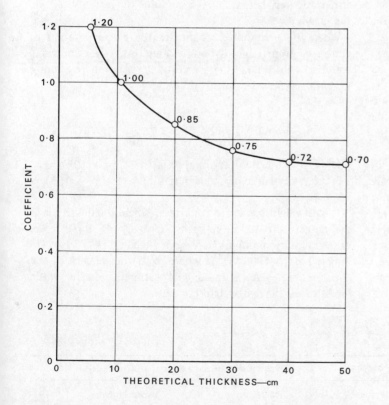

Figure 6.12 : Creep coefficient for the size of a concrete member. (The theoretical thickness is the quotient of the area of the section divided by half the perimeter in contact with the atmosphere.)

Experimental work suggests the drying shrinkage of light-weight aggregate concrete is between one and two times that of dense natural aggregate concrete.

One important factor not discussed so far is the very significant effect the particular source of natural aggregate may have on the drying shrinkage of the concrete. Aggregates leading to a particularly high drying shrinkage are limited to certain geographical locations; in the United Kingdom they appear to be limited to central Scotland and to the extreme north of England. The following recommendations are drawn from a report[63] on research into the shrinkage of concretes made with a wide range of Scottish aggregates. It is important to note that the numerical values relate only to the particular test procedure adopted for the research.

(1) Some very hard quartz, flint gravel and marble aggregates are virtually non-shrinking and produce concretes having a drying shrinkage less than 0.025%.

(2) Drying shrinkage values below 0.045% are produced with several types of low-shrinkage aggregate such as granite, limestone, unaltered felsite, blastfurnace slag and a few dolerites and gabbros. These are thought suitable for all in situ and most precast concreting.

(3) Most of the aggregates in central Scotland produce concretes of drying shrinkage in the range 0.046% to 0.065%. These materials are thought suitable for most purposes, though special care is needed in the design of such units as cladding panels and cast in situ floors, particularly if used in structures due to be heated. Special consideration should be given to deflections in beams and to prestressing losses.

(4) A wide range of aggregates can lead to drying shrinkage values in the range 0.066% to 0.085%, and the durability of the concrete is thought suspect at the upper end of the range. Although the aggregates are suitable for use, air entrainment is thought advisable for unreinforced or thin members exposed to the weather.

(5) Drying shrinkage values over 0.085% occur mainly with some sedimentary rocks such as grey wacke, shale and mudstone. Severe warping and deterioration of the concrete has been noted and the aggregates are therefore thought suitable only for applications where the concrete never dries out, for mass concrete surfaced with air-entrained concrete, and for members that are symmetrically and heavily reinforced and are not exposed to the weather.

(6) Different batches of ordinary Portland cement can give rise to differences in drying shrinkage of 0.005% in the concrete. Although coarse aggregate has a predominant effect on drying shrinkage, the fine aggregate also has an effect, up to 0.003%, when concrete with a high-shrinkage coarse and fine aggregate is compared with one with the same coarse aggregate but a low-shrinkage fine aggregate.

6.14 Elasticity and creep

6.14.1 Modulus of elasticity

The elasticity of concrete is primarily dependent on the compressive strength of the concrete and the properties of the aggregate; to a lesser extent it is dependent on the environment in which the concrete is placed, the mix proportions and the type of cement. For most purposes the values given in Table 6.9 can be adopted for concretes made with natural aggregates and having a density of 2300 kg/m^3 (145 lb/ft^3) or more. If a more accurate figure is required for particular constituent materials and mix proportions, tests should be made in accordance with BS 1881. Concretes made from a few particular sources of constituent materials may have a modulus of elasticity outside the ranges given in Table 6.9.

When it is required to estimate the static modulus of concrete from the dynamic modulus, the following equation will generally give an estimate accurate to about 4 kN/mm^2 (0.58 x 10^6 lbf/in^2):

$$E_c = 1.25 E_d - 19$$
$$\text{(in imperial units, } E_c = 1.25 E_d - 2.75)$$

where E_c = static modulus in kN/mm^2 (lbf/in^2 x 10^6);
E_d = dynamic modulus in kN/mm^2 (lbf/in^2 x 10^6).

For lightweight aggregate concretes, where the density is in the range 1440 to 2300 kg/m^3 (90 to 145 lb/ft^3), the values of static modulus may be reduced by $(W/2300)^2$ (in imperial units $(W/145)^2$), where W is the density of the concrete, to give a reasonable estimate of the static modulus for the lightweight concrete.

TABLE 6.9
Moduli of elasticity.

Compressive strength – N/mm^2 (lbf/in^2)	Static modulus – kN/mm^2 (lbf/in^2 x 10^6)		Dynamic modulus – kN/mm^2 (lbf/in^2 x 10^6)	
	Mean value	Typical range	Mean value	Typical range
20 (2900)	25 (3.6)	21-29 (3.0-4.2)	35 (5.1)	31-39 (4.5-5.7)
25 (3600)	26 (3.8)	22-30 (3.2-4.4)	36 (5.2)	32-40 (4.6-5.8)
30 (4350)	28 (4.1)	23-33 (3.3-4.8)	38 (5.5)	33-43 (4.8-6.2)
40 (5800)	31 (4.5)	26-36 (3.8-5.2)	40 (5.8)	35-45 (5.1-6.5)
50 (7250)	34 (4.9)	28-40 (4.1-5.8)	42 (6.1)	36-48 (5.2-7.0)
60 (8700)	36 (5.2)	30-42 (4.4-6.1)	44 (6.4)	38-50 (5.5-7.2)

6.14.2 Creep

Concrete under stress undergoes a gradual increase in strain with time. This is due to the effect of creep, which is defined as the increase in strain under sustained stress. Creep is also responsible for a gradual loss of stress in concrete subject to a particular strain. This relaxation of stress is of particular importance in prestressed concrete structures and can account for a considerable proportion of prestressing losses.

Many factors affect the creep of concrete, including the relative humidity in which the concrete is kept, the age of the concrete at the time of loading, the mix proportions of the concrete, the size of the member being considered and the duration of loading. These factors have been related in the CEB-FIP Recommendations[7], where the creep is expressed as a proportion of the elastic strain to which the concrete is subjected on loading. The numerical value of creep is the product of the ordinates to Figures 6.10, 6.7, 6.9, 6.11 and 6.12; it is interesting to note that two of the graphs (Figures 6.7 and 6.9) are common to drying shrinkage and creep. As with the estimates of drying shrinkage already discussed, the estimate of final creep must be treated with some reserve because of the likely effect of some other variables not included.

6.15 Watertight concrete

Concrete can prove not to be watertight in a number of ways, including excessive permeability, inadequate compaction, cracking; other factors, including faulty construction joints, do not come within the scope of this book.

The permeability of concrete was discussed at some length in Chapter 5 and also, in regard to admixtures, in Chapter 3.4. The primary requirements for a concrete having a low permeability are a low water/cement ratio, full compaction and good curing; in comparison, other factors such as the possible inclusion of admixtures are relatively unimportant. Indeed, for the vast majority of applications, concrete of good quality can be regarded as being virtually impermeable.

A lack of watertightness in concrete is more likely to result from cracking than from high permeability. Cracking is caused by stress in the concrete which can be brought about by temperature changes in the early-age concrete following the development of heat of hydration, temperature changes following different weather conditions, drying shrinkage and loading. All but the first of these should be accounted for by good structural design incorporating the correct amount and spacing of reinforcement. The first factor is, however, not so easily controlled, largely because the bond strength between concrete and reinforcement has only partly built up at the time the stresses are developed. It is for this reason that the temperature rise in concrete due to the development of heat of hydration must be controlled in thick concrete members where watertightness is important.

The principal means of limiting the temperature rise of a concrete specified to have a particular minimum strength are good quality control (leading to a lower strength margin and thus a lower cement content), large aggregate maximum size and low concrete workability (both leading to a lower cement content), the use of water-reducing admixtures or the partial replacement of the cement by pulverized-fuel ash (provided high early-age strengths are not required of the concrete). Certain aspects of construction can also reduce the temperature rise; examples are the use of shallow lifts, the cooling of the fresh concrete or the use of non-insulating types of formwork.

6.16 Thermal characteristics of hardened concrete

6.16.1 Thermal conductivity

The thermal conductivity of concrete is dependent primarily upon the type of aggregate used and the moisture content of the hardened concrete. With the use of dense aggregate, it is typically in the range 1.15 to 1.45 W/m°C (8.0 to 10.0 Btu in/ft^2 h °F). Aggregates composed largely of quartz tend to give the highest values whereas basalts, gabbros and blastfurnace slag tend to give the lowest values. Limestones and granites give intermediate values, though limestones vary widely from one source to another. The conductivity of dry concrete may be as much as 33% below that of saturated concrete; the higher the conductivity of the concrete, the greater the decrease. Neither a change in the mix proportions nor a change in the temperature appears to influence the thermal conductivity to any great extent.

One of the properties often justifying the use of lightweight aggregate concrete[60] is its low thermal conductivity and therefore good thermal insulation. The reduction in conductivity is due to the inclusion of air in the concrete, usually resulting from the cellular nature of the aggregate particles. The entrainment of air in the cement paste has a similar effect, depending upon the quantity of air entrained. Since the density of the concrete is also affected by the inclusion of air it follows that a reasonable, though not unique, relation exists between the thermal conductivity and the density of the concrete. This approximate relation, for different types of lightweight aggregate available in the United Kingdom, is shown in Figure 6.13.

Since heat is conducted through water about 25 times as fast as through air, the true conductivity values at different moisture contents must be obtained by multiplying the oven-dry value by a factor, f, depending upon the moisture content. Values of this factor are given in Table 6.10. The selection of an appropriate type of lightweight aggregate and an appropriate density must therefore be preceded by an assessment of the likely moisture content of the concrete during the working life of the structure. Typically such moisture contents by volume will be very low for concrete in heated buildings not subject to driving rain.

6.16.2 Thermal expansion

The coefficient of thermal expansion of concrete varies to a considerable extent, depending principally on the geological type of aggregate used and particularly on its silica content.[64] Browne[65] has summarized the results of several research projects, which are given in Table 6.11. The large variations existing within any one group show, however, that it is not possible to predict more than very approximately the coefficient of thermal expansion from the geological rock type. The coefficient also varies with the amount of moisture present, being greatest at about 70% relative humidity and somewhat less when the concrete is either saturated or fully dried. If an accurate prediction of the coefficient of thermal expansion is required, this must be measured on test specimens made from trial mixes, keeping in mind that the mix proportions will affect the value to some extent.

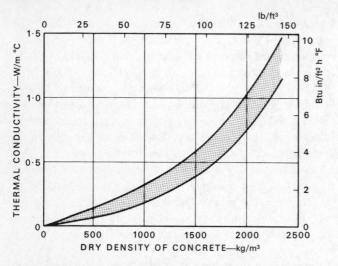

Figure 6.13 : Approximate relation between dry density of concrete and thermal conductivity.

TABLE 6.10
Multiplication factor (f) for thermal conductivity due to changes in moisture content.

Moisture content by volume – %	1	2.55	5	10	15	20	25
Factor f	1.3	1.55	1.75	2.10	2.35	2.55	2.75

The coefficient of thermal expansion of lightweight aggregate concretes tends to be about 20% lower than that for most normal concretes made with aggregate containing a high proportion of silica; a value of 8×10^{-6} per °C has sometimes been assumed.

6.17   Concrete subject to high temperatures

Concrete has a good resistance to short-period high temperatures such as those which may occur in accidental fires; this applies particularly to concretes made with lightweight or limestone aggregate. However, in applications where concrete is to be deliberately subjected to sustained high temperatures, such as may occur in some industrial installations, or to sharp changes in temperature, such as in foundry floors subject to spillage of molten metal, the properties of both concrete and aggregate must be taken into account.

TABLE 6.11
Variation of aggregate type and coefficient of thermal expansion of concrete.

Rock (geological group)	Typical silica content of rock (% by weight)	Range of coefficients of thermal expansion of concretes $-10^{-6}/°C$
chert	94	11.4-12.2
quartzite	94	11.7-14.6
quartz	94	9.0-13.2
sandstone	84	9.2-13.3
marble	negligible	4.1-7.4
siliceous limestone	45	8.1-11.0
granite	66	8.1-10.3
basalt	51	7.9-10.4
limestone	negligible	4.3-10.3
gravel	5-95	9.0-13.7

Some siliceous aggregates undergo a marked volume expansion at temperatures about 250°C; if such aggregates are heated rapidly through this temperature, the larger particles may shatter explosively. Siliceous aggregates should therefore not be used where temperatures in excess of 250°C are likely to occur. Limestone aggregates do not react in this way and may be used at higher temperatures up to about 500°C. If heated for a prolonged period above this temperature, however, they may slowly decompose forming calcium oxide (quicklime) which on subsequent cooling forms calcium hydroxide and swells. Fine-grained igneous rocks, in which any siliceous components are finely divided, are generally stable both chemically and physically and have been used at temperatures up to about 900°C.

Clean broken brick also provides an acceptable aggregate for concrete which is to be subjected to high temperatures because, having been made by firing to about 1000°C, it will rarely undergo any serious chemical or physical change below this temperature. Firebricks are made by firing special clays at temperatures higher than 1000°C; when crushed to form aggregate, they can be used in refractory concretes for use up to 1350°C.

All hydraulic cement concretes suffer a loss in strength as the chemically bound water is driven off at high temperatures. In the case of Portland and high alumina cement concretes there is usually sufficient residual strength for refractory purposes. In supersulphated cement concrete so much water of hydration is lost that the cement is of little use for high-temperature work.

It is usual, however, to limit Portland cement concrete to applications where sustained temperatures do not exceed about 300°C. This is because significant quantities of calcium oxide may be released at high temperatures with a similar result to that already noted for some limestone aggregates. The concrete also undergoes a considerable shrinkage at about this temperature. High alumina cement concretes are not subject to this limitation, and ordinary grey high alumina cement is commonly used with firebrick aggregate to make refractory concrete which will withstand temperatures of 1300 to 1350°C. A special high-purity white high alumina cement is available which, when used with an appropriate artificial refractory aggregate, can be used up to 1800°C.

It should be noted that concrete which is intended to serve at high temperatures should not be relied on to withstand superimposed loads and should therefore be separate from the load-carrying structure which should remain at more normal temperatures.

6.18 High alumina cement

High alumina cement is likely to be used in concrete which is required to have high resistance to sulphates and weak acids or to refractory temperatures, and it is often these considerations which will affect the choice of aggregate and the mix proportions. In other applications it is the very rapid rate of strength gain in the first days after casting that is of particular importance.

The use of the cement requires careful consideration because a high proportion of the heat of hydration is released in the first day after casting and this can lead to an excessive build-up of temperature and subsequently to cracking on cooling. Another limitation on the use of high alumina cement arises because of the possibility of conversion of the hydrate to a chemically more stable but more porous form. The change is more likely to occur if the concrete reaches a temperature of 25 to 30°C or more while in damp conditions. The rate of conversion is, however, very largely dependent upon the water/cement ratio of the concrete and the maximum sustained temperature at which the concrete is intended to serve; it may prove to be negligible for well-cured concrete exposed to normal temperature and humidity. To offset the possible adverse effects of conversion, a maximum free water/cement ratio of 0.4 and a characteristic compressive strength of 50 N/mm² (7250 lbf/in²) at one day are recommended for reinforced concrete work in the United Kingdom; for concrete which is to be kept in a warm, damp environment, for example in tropical climates, a maximum water/cement ratio of 0.35 would often be advisable. For prestressed concrete, a maximum free water/cement ratio of 0.35 and a characteristic compressive strength of 60 N/mm² (8700 lbf/in²) at one day would often be appropriate.

Under adverse conditions the converted strength can be as much as 30 N/mm² (4350 lbf/in²) below the strength at 24 hours at 18°C, except where the free water/cement ratio is very low, say 0.3, where the difference is somewhat less. Therefore, when it is thought likely that the concrete will convert as a result of the enviroment in which it is to be placed, the characteristic strength should be increased by up to 30 N/mm² (4350 lbf/in²) as well as by the normal margin required to allow for site variations, in order to arrive at the target mean strength at 24 hours. Data reported by Newman[66], or the recommendations given in the Handbook to CP 110[67], can be used for the design of high alumina cement concrete mixes. The presentation of the data and the method of use is very similar to that for Portland cement concretes given in Chapter 4.4. The free water/cement ratio required to give the target mean strength is determined from Figure 6.14, taken from[67].

This figure includes data for the strength at 1 day and also for the fully converted strength of the concrete.

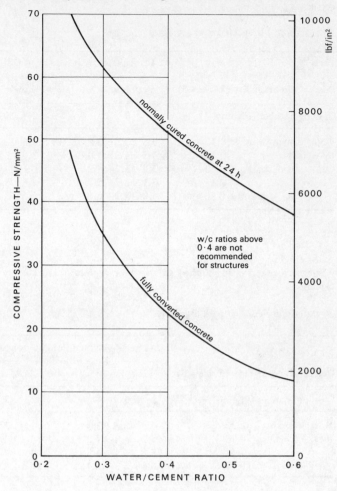

Figure 6.14 : Relation between compressive strength and water/cement ratio for high alumina cement concrete.

Once the free water/cement ratio has been assessed, the relation between this, the workability, the grading and the aggregate/cement ratio can be found in Tables 6.12 and 6.13 which refer to 20 mm (¾ in.) maximum-size irregular gravel and crushed rock aggregates respectively. A comparison with Tables 4.8 and 4.9 respectively shows that, to obtain a particular workability and water/cement ratio, high alumina cement mixes tend to have a higher aggregate/cement ratio (lower cement content) than those made with Portland cement. This applies more particularly to low workabilities and low water/cement ratios. High alumina cement concrete not only possesses better workability characteristics than Portland cement concrete of similar proportions, but is also more liable to segregate during mixing and handling. For this reason it is not generally recommended for use with a low proportion of fine aggregate to total aggregate; Tables 6.12 and 6.13 therefore restrict aggregate gradings to numbers 2, 3 and 4 of Figure 4.4. Once the aggregate/cement ratio and grading needed to meet the required water/cement ratio and workability have been estimated from Table 6.12 or 6.13, it is advisable to calculate the cement content in the manner described in Chapter 7.3.2 and then to check this value against any specification requirement — for example, a requirement for

TABLE 6.12
Aggregate/cement ratio required to give four degrees of workability with different water/cement ratios and gradings using high alumina cement.

20 mm (¾ in.) irregular gravel aggregate

		Aggregate/cement ratio by weight											
Degree of workability (Table 4.3)		'Very low'			'Low'			'Medium'			'High'		
Grading number (Figure 4.4)		2	3	4	2	3	4	2	3	4	2	3	4
Water/cement ratio by weight	0.30	3.5	3.5	3.0	2.8	2.8	2.5						
	0.35	4.5	4.3	4.0	3.7	3.6	3.3	3.0	3.0	2.7	2.5	2.6	2.4
	0.40	5.7	5.2	4.9	4.6	4.4	4.2	3.7	3.7	3.5	3.3	3.3	3.1
	0.45	7.1	6.2	5.7	5.6	5.3	4.9	4.3	4.4	4.2	3.9	3.9	3.9
	0.50	8.0	7.2	6.5	6.6	6.0	5.4	5.1	5.0	4.8	4.6	4.6	4.5

TABLE 6.13
Aggregate/cement ratio required to give four degrees of workability with different water/cement ratios and gradings using high alumina cement.

20 mm (¾ in.) crushed rock aggregate

		Aggregate/cement ratio by weight											
Degree of workability (Table 4.3)		'Very low'			'Low'			'Medium'			'High'		
Grading number (Figure 4.4)		2	3	4	2	3	4	2	3	4	2	3	4
Water/cement ratio by weight	0.35	4.2	3.8	3.6	3.0	2.9	2.7						
	0.40	5.2	4.4	4.2	4.3	3.8	3.6	3.6	3.2	3.0	3.0	2.9	2.7
	0.45	5.8	5.1	4.8	4.8	4.3	4.1	4.0	3.7	3.5	3.7	3.4	3.3
	0.50	6.4	5.7	5.4	5.3	4.9	4.6	4.4	4.2	3.9	4.0	3.9	3.6

sulphate resistance (see Table 5.4). If the cement content is unacceptably high or low, the mix proportions will need to be modified; any gross inconsistencies may require the nature of the construction work or the method of construction, or the choice of constituent materials, to be reconsidered.

If the estimated mix proportions appear reasonable, they should be verified by means of trial mixes (see Chapter 7). Where it is necessary to estimate mix proportions for aggregates of maximum sizes other than 20 mm (¾ in.), it will be necessary to extrapolate from the data presented and to make several trial mixes of different mix proportions so that the most appropriate mix can be selected for the construction work. One advantage of high alumina cement is that strength test results are generally obtained 24 hours after the trial mixes are made, so that a repeat trial mix is of no great disadvantage.

6.19 Supersulphated cement

The selection of the constituent materials and mix proportions when supersulphated cement is used is in many respects similar to that when Portland cement is used, though there are several important differences to note.

Supersulphated cement is likely to be used in circumstances where the concrete is to be exposed to aggressive chemicals; see, for example, Chapter 5.4. It is therefore important that the concrete should be of low permeability, and for this reason the water/cement ratio should be kept low; in practice, water/cement ratios should not exceed 0.45 and, in order that the concrete should have adequate workability for full compaction, the cement content should not be less than 270 kg/m^3 (450 lb/yd^3) for 40 mm (1½ in.) maximum-size aggregate, 310 kg/m^3 (520 lb/yd^3) for 20 mm (¾ in.) aggregate or 360 kg/m^3 (610 lb/yd^3) for 10 mm (3/8 in.) aggregate.

Further, it is important that the aggregate should be of good quality and the fine aggregate should be of relatively coarse grading, generally complying with grading zones 1 or 2 of BS 882. Finer gradings of fine aggregate are liable to lead to the use of higher water/cement ratios than are desirable. For the same reason the proportion of fine aggregate to total aggregate should be kept fairly low and, as a guide line, the proportion of aggregate passing a 2.36 mm (No. 7) sieve should not exceed 30% by weight of the total aggregate. Such low proportions of fine aggregate are acceptable because supersulphated cement tends to produce a rather more cohesive concrete than would a Portland cement used in otherwise similar mixes.

The relation between compressive strength at 28 days to water/cement ratio is similar to that given in Figure 4.2 for ordinary Portland cement; this same relation may be used to select mix proportions for trial mixes. The relations between mix proportions and workability given in Tables 4.3 to 4.11 for Portland cement are applicable to super-sulphated cement concrete only for those figures relating to type gradings 1 and 2 (given in Figures 4.3 to 4.5). Whatever the mix proportions selected on the basis of a required strength, they are subject to the limiting values for durability requirements given in Chapter 5 and to verification by means of trial mixes (see Chapter 7).

Admixtures based on lignosulphonic acid can be of particular advantage with supersulphated cement, provided they are free of sugar-like compounds. Not only can the water/cement ratio be reduced without loss of workability, but there is less loss of workability following prolonged agitation of the concrete, as could occur with ready-mixed concrete.

6.20   Lean concrete bases

Lean concrete is widely used as a base material on which further construction can proceed over ground of low bearing capacity, or as a reliable base to flexible surfacing in road construction.[68-70] It is generally compacted by rolling, though several other techniques are sometimes used. The material has much in common with soil-cement and cement-bound granular material, which are composed of selected, but unprocessed, soil and granular material, whereas lean concrete contains a processed aggregate. In the case of the other materials, control over quality is exercised

largely by careful and often extensive testing, whereas lean concrete is more easily controlled by having processed aggregate. A further important distinction is that lean concrete can normally be mixed in a conventional free-fall concrete mixer, whereas the other materials generally require a paddle-type or other special mixer.

Aggregates should therefore comply with BS 882, and are generally of 40 mm (1½ in.) nominal maximum size. Larger maximum sizes have been used, though it is less easy to obtain a good surface regularity of the compacted concrete. The aggregate should be continuously graded; it is usually found that gradings within the limits given in Figure 6.15 give the best results. Although an approximate limit of 6% is suggested for the 150 μm (No. 100) sieve size, up to 10% has been used without difficulty. The limits for clay and silt content given in BS 882 can be relaxed slightly, provided the final material is of a type that will mix with the cement in a concrete mixer; lumps of clay are not acceptable. Coarse aggregate containing a high proportion of soft particles which crush under the action of a roller should also be avoided.

The cement should comply with BS 12 or BS 146. If the concrete is required to be opened to traffic at an early age, rapid-hardening Portland cement or extra rapid-hardening cement may be used.

The workability of lean concrete is governed by the method of compaction adopted. If the concrete is compacted by rolling, the workability should be such that the concrete is just mouldable in the hands; another way to describe it is to say that the concrete should be reasonably wet but not so wet as to allow the roller to sink during compaction. Typically this workability corresponds to a total water content of about 6% by weight of all solid

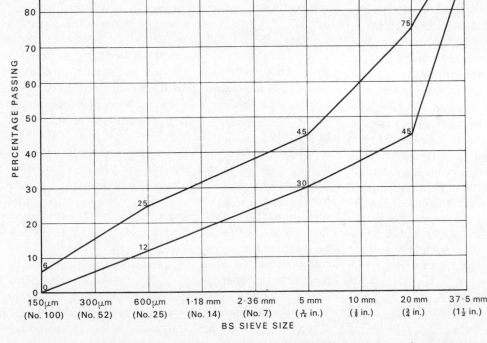

Figure 6.15 : Grading envelope for lean concrete using 40 mm (1½ in.) maximum-size aggregate.

constituents. If the concrete is significantly drier than this, it is likely that full compaction will not be obtained; full compaction is usually described as a dry density of not less than 95% of the maximum obtainable theoretical dry density of the material as compacted to zero air voids. If the lean concrete is to be compacted by vibrating beams or by immersion vibrators, a rather higher workability should be used.

The strength of lean concrete should be determined in accordance with BS 1881, except that concretes of a workability appropriate for rolling should be compacted in a 150 mm (6 in.) cube mould by means of an electric or pneumatic hammer with a square or rectangular foot having an area of 1 to 1.5 dm^2 (16 to 23 in^2) applied directly to each of three layers of the concrete to compact it to refusal; this technique is necessary to avoid excessive variation in the density of the test specimens. Strength specifications vary, often giving a 28-day strength of about 10 N/mm^2 (1450 lbf/in^2) as the figure below which not more than 20% of the test results may fall. The target mean strength with good quality control is typically 12 N/mm^2 (1750 lbf/in^2).

The aggregate/cement ratios used in practice are generally between 15 and 20 by weight. It is therefore convenient in many instances to make two trial mixes with these proportions, using the workability appropriate to the method of compaction to be used on site. When making the trial mixes, it is important that the total moisture content of the aggregate and the amount of water added to the mix should be known. The density of the fresh concrete should be measured and the dry density of the concrete calculated. This density should then be compared with the theoretical dry density as calculated from the dry weights of cement and aggregate, the specific gravity of cement (which may be taken as 3.1) and the apparent specific gravity of the coarse and fine aggregates as defined and measured in accordance with BS 812.

The dry density determined from the trial mix would generally be 97 to 98% of the theoretical dry density for concrete of relatively low workability which is to be compacted by rolling, and 98 to 99% for more workable concrete to be compacted by a vibrating beam; if these densities are not achieved, slight adjustments may have to be made to the mix proportions and probably to the water content or the proportion of fine aggregate. Provided the densities are satisfactory, the mix proportions are based on the compressive strengths obtained for the trial mixes, interpolating if necessary. If the compressive strength results are too low, or unusually high, it will be necessary to adjust the mix proportions further or to change the source of constituent materials. If the strength is still too high with an aggregate/cement ratio of 20, leaner mixes may be permitted by the specification, though it is not unlikely that the conventional free-fall mixer will prove unsatisfactory and have to be replaced by, for example, a pan mixer.

Example of calculation of theoretical dry density

Given: aggregate/cement ratio = 20
  water as proportion of aggregate
    and cement = 6%
  proportion of fine in total aggregate = 35%
  apparent specific gravity of fine
    aggregate = 2.65
  apparent specific gravity of coarse
    aggregate = 2.60

Weight of materials
  cement = 1.00 (basis)
  fine aggregate = 20 x 35/100 = 7.00
  coarse aggregate = 20 − 7.00 = 13.00
  weight of dry lean concrete = 21.00

Volume of materials
  cement = 1.00/3.12 = 0.32
  fine aggregates = 7.00/2.65 = 2.64
  coarse aggregate = 13.00/2.60 = 5.00
  water = (6/100) x (20 + 1) = 1.26
  lean concrete = 9.22

Density of lean concrete
  theoretical maximum dry density
    = (21.00/9.22) x 1000 = 2280 kg/m^3
    (in imperial units: (21.00/9.22) x 62.4 = 142 lb/ft^3)
  95% of maximum dry density
    = 0.95 x 2280 = 2160 kg/m^3
    (in imperial units: 0.95 x 142 = 135 lb/ft^3)

6.21 Concrete blocks

Blocks made with concrete containing coarse aggregate cannot be subject to the normal process of mix design. This is partly because of the properties required of the blocks and partly because of the process by which the blocks are cast.[71, 72] As a result, greater dependence than usual has to be placed on full-scale trial mixes before the most suitable mixes can be found. Blocks specified to BS 2028 are required to attain a relatively low strength and yet to have the best possible thermal insulating properties; to be easy to handle they must be made as lightweight as is reasonably possible, often to a density of 1700 to 1900 kg/m^3 (105 to 120 lb/ft^3). The requirement for light weight often leads to the use of lightweight aggregate instead of dense natural aggregate, and therefore to lower densities. The other means by which some blocks are made light in weight is that they are not fully compacted in the sense in which full compaction is usually understood, and they often contain 20 to 30% voids and have an open-textured surface.

Most blocks are precast by mass-production machines of the pallet or egg-laying types. The blocks are demoulded immediately after compaction and are then subject to handling. They must therefore have considerable 'green' strength if they are not to deform outside the permitted tolerances. In practice this requirement for green strength means that the water content of the concrete is critical and cannot be deliberately varied by much or allowed to vary during normal production runs.

One important property required of concrete blocks is that they should not be subject to excessive drying shrinkage which could lead to cracking of block walls. This property is sufficiently critical to be taken into account in selecting the method of production and the mix proportions. Blocks stored in damp conditions tend to have a higher drying shrinkage, whereas blocks which are autoclaved tend to have a significantly lower drying shrinkage than those which dry out in normal room conditions. Steam curing at normal atmospheric pressure has little effect on the drying shrinkage.

Cement paste has a high shrinkage, which is generally restrained by the inclusion of coarse aggregate. Experience shows that, for dense aggregate blocks, aggregate/cement ratios between 8 and 10 by weight are necessary to limit the drying shrinkage. With lightweight concrete, approximately similar cement contents are used, though rather higher drying shrinkage values are obtained and are permitted by BS 2028.

Once the proportion of cement has been fixed as largely dependent upon the drying shrinkage, the strength and density of the hardened block, and the strength of the green block, must be controlled by the choice of aggregate type, maximum size and grading, and by the amount of compactive effort applied to the block during production. In many production machines, where the concrete is compressed into a fixed size of mould, the quantity of concrete initially put into the mould must be carefully controlled.

The maximum size of aggregate should be as large as possible and is generally about 10 mm (3/8 in.), though for solid blocks 14 mm (½ in.) aggregate can be used, and in hollow or facing blocks a smaller size may be necessary. Angular aggregate tends to give a better green strength than aggregate of round particle shape. The best aggregate grading must be found by trials, but as a first approximation a straight-line grading curve between the maximum size of aggregate at 100% passing and the 150 μm (No. 100) sieve at 0% passing can be assumed.

6.22 Curing at high and low temperatures

6.22.1 Principles

The rate at which chemical reactions take place is influenced by temperature, and the hydration of Portland cement is no exception. Within limits, the reaction takes place more quickly as the temperature is raised and more slowly as the temperature is reduced. If the temperature of the concrete in °C is plotted against time in hours, than the area under the curve is a measure of the amount of chemical activity which has taken place up to that time. This chemical activity would be shown by one of several factors, including the amount of heat of hydration evolved or, more usually, by the compressive strength of the concrete. The area under the curve is usually called the maturity and is expressed in units of °C h.[73, 74]

The basis of temperature from which the maturity of concrete is calculated is generally taken as −10°C, which is accepted in this book. The compressive strengths are, unless otherwise stated, associated with a temperature of 16°C, and it is therefore possible to calculate a value for maturity associated with any particular age of concrete. For example, the maturity of concrete at 7 days, working from a datum −10°C, is 7 days x 24 hours x (16 + 10)°C = 4368°C h. If it is required to know the age in days at which the same concrete mix could reach the same strength but at a different temperature, this can easily be calculated by dividing the value 4368 by the product of the new temperature (relative to the same datum of −10°C) and 24 hours. This can be more generally expressed as

$$T_2 = \frac{(16 + 10)}{(\theta + 10)} T_1$$

where T_1 = age of concrete subject to curing at 16°C
and T_2 = age of concrete subject to curing at a temperature of θ°C.

This formula is, of course, subject to a number of limitations, of which the most obvious are that the concrete must neither freeze nor boil and must be kept in a damp environment. A practical limitation on the usefulness of the formula is the fact that temperatures are not steady and it is difficult to estimate the average temperature at which the concrete will be kept. Nevertheless, the formula has its uses in arriving at a mix design for concrete to be maintained at a temperature other than 16°C and in judging the rate at which it will harden. The approximations associated with the formula have the effect that it is not worth making any adjustment for concrete maintained between about 12°C and 20°C.

There is some evidence[75, 76] to suggest that the above formula is unsatisfactory for low maturities. For determining the striking time of formwork an alternative formula, relating time and temperature for a given concrete and a particular strength level, is more appropriate; this formula is

$$T_1 (\theta_1 + 16)^2 = T_2 (\theta_2 + 16)^2$$

where T_1 and T_2 are, respectively, the ages of concrete cured at temperatures θ_1 and θ_2.

If concrete cubes are kept alongside a structural member at a temperature significantly differing from the 20°C required for test cubes, it is important to realize that they will only give an approximate indication of the strength of the concrete in the structure. Significant errors are liable to arise because the temperature inside a small mass like a cube is much less affected by the heat of hydration than that developed in a relatively large mass of concrete. In general, cubes cured in this way will underestimate the strength of the concrete in the structure; they will also exhibit greater variation in strength than cubes cured under standard conditions, and it is therefore not appropriate to use such test results to judge either the variability of the concrete or its compliance with the job specification.

6.22.2 Steam curing at atmospheric pressure

A significant proportion of concrete is cured, for the first few hours after casting, by steam at a temperature approaching 100°C. The principal benefit derived is that it is possible to demould concrete units sooner than if more normal temperatures had been used, and to make more rapid re-use of the moulds for casting further units. A frequent rate of re-use is 24 hours.

The concept of maturity just discussed can be applied, though there is a further limitation in that if the rate of temperature rise is too fast the ultimate strength of the concrete will suffer. It has been suggested that the temperature of the concrete should not exceed 50°C in the first 2 hours after casting, nor 100°C in the first 6 hours.

An example of a maturity curve for steam curing at atmospheric pressure is shown in Figure 6.16. The temperature of casting is taken as 15°C; it is then proposed to raise the temperature to reach a value of 85°C 6 hours after casting, to maintain this temperature for a further 6 hours, and thereafter to conserve the heat by merely enclosing the unit and allowing the temperature to drop by 20°C over the next 6 hours, after which the concrete is demoulded. It is sufficiently accurate to join the points in Figure 6.16 by straight lines. The maturity reached after 18 hours is 1440°C h, and this is the equivalent of 1440/(16 + 10) = 55 hours' or 2½ days' curing at 16°C. The compressive strength of the concrete required for satisfactory demoulding will be known, and it is then possible to design a suitable mix, interpolating the data in Chapter 4.

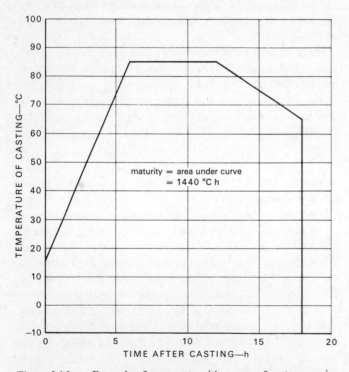

Figure 6.16 : Example of temperature/time curve for steam curing of concrete at atmospheric pressure.

Steam curing can be used at pressures greater than atmospheric, which will enable temperatures in excess of 100°C to be used. However, this is a specialized technique used by some precast concrete manufacturers where conventional mix design data cannot be used. It is therefore regarded as being beyond the scope of this book.

6.22.3 Hot concrete

The technique has been developed, in recent years, of producing fresh concrete at a temperature around 60°C[77]; as would be expected, the concrete loses workability rapidly and has to be placed very quickly after mixing. The high temperature is achieved by injecting steam into the concrete while mixing is taking place. The steam is injected from the back of the mixing blades or by a similar techique in an otherwise conventional pan mixer. Typically half the mixing water (excluding the moisture in the aggregates) might be added to the concrete in the form of steam; as an approximation, it can be assumed that 1 kg (1.7 lb) of steam will be required to raise the temperature of 1 m³ (1 yd³) of concrete through 1°C. The fact that the concrete achieves such high temperatures before it is compacted in the mould does not appear to have a serious deleterious effect on the ultimate strength, though the adequacy of the strength must be carefully checked by trials. With this technique, the maturity of concrete can be considerably greater than that achieved by more normal steam curing methods.

6.22.4 Winter concreting

In winter the rate at which concrete sets and hardens is considerably retarded. Provided the concrete does not freeze and is kept damp, retardation will not detract from the longer-term satisfactory performance of the concrete. The slowing down of the hardening will, however, be likely to increase the cost of the work by lengthening the time before formwork can be struck and before subsequent lifts of concrete can be placed. Further, protection of the concrete from freezing is an added expense. The careful selection of the concrete constituents and mix proportions can often reduce delays very considerably.

Concrete designed to have a characteristic strength of 20 N/mm² (2900 lbf/in²) or more at 28 days will generally not be adversely affected by winter conditions in the United Kingdom after it has reached a compressive strength of about 5 N/mm² (720 lbf/in²) and provided the concrete is not saturated. Saturation can be avoided by curing, using the technique of retaining the mixing water within the concrete rather than applying further water. Since the time at which a strength of 5 N/mm² (720 lbf/in²) will be reached depends upon the potential strength of the concrete, it is convenient to work from a value of maturity which has been proved satisfactory by past experience. Approximate values are given in Table 6.14, where the maturity is based on −10°C and starts from the time the concrete first stiffens and not from the time of placing. These maturities are achieved during the so-called 'prehardening' period.[78] Later research[75, 76] suggests these pre-hardening periods should be increased at lower

TABLE 6.14
Requisite pre-hardening periods for ordinary Portland cement concrete without an accelerating admixture.

	Requisite pre-hardening period*		
		at stated concrete temperature – h	
Specified minimum strength at 28 days using ordinary Portland cement – N/mm² (lbf/in²)	at a concrete temperature greater than 5 °C in units of maturity (°C h)	20°C	10°C
20 (2900)	1030	34	52
25 (3600)	780	26	39
30 (4350)	630	21	32
40 (5800)	480	16	24

*The pre-hardening periods are reduced to the following when the rate of hardening is accelerated by using:

extra-rapid-hardening Portland cement	40%
rapid-hardening Portland cement	60%
ordinary Portland cement with 1.5% anhydrous calcium chloride	75%
rapid-hardening Portland cement with 1.5% anhydrous calcium chloride	45%

temperatures, so when accurate results are required the original research data should be examined.

If the construction programme on site has been fixed and it is intended to carry on with the work despite low temperatures, the data can be used in various ways to determine by how much the pre-hardening period could be reduced. The most economical solution can probably be determined by comparing the following alternatives:

(1) a different cement, or calcium chloride, might be used;

(2) a minimum curing temperature could be maintained by employing better insulation or by heating the concrete; or

(3) a higher 28-day minimum compressive strength could be used.

The other major effect of low temperature in winter building is the generally longer periods required before formwork can be struck. Provided satisfactory striking times are known for normal weather conditions, maturity calculations can be used to calculate appropriate times at other temperatures. It may be appropriate to maintain better insulation round the concrete or to apply some heat; in either case, once the temperature is known the striking time can be calculated. The benefits of using different cements and/or calcium chloride are similar to the benefits already shown for reducing the pre-hardening period. he effects of using a higher-strength concrete would have to be assessed from data on the development of concrete strength with age, such as those given in Chapter 4.

6.23 Concrete for pumping

For the successful pumping of a concrete through a pipeline, a considerable number of conditions should be observed with regard to the constituent materials and the mix proportions of the concrete.[34] These conditions are as follows.

(1) It is essential that the pressure in the pipeline is transmitted through the concrete via the water in the mix and not via the aggregate; in effect, this ensures the pipeline is lubricated. If pressure is applied via the aggregate it is highly likely that the aggregate particles will compact together and against the inside of the pipe to form a blockage; the force required to move concrete under these conditions is several hundred times that required for a lubricated mix.

(2) If, however, pressure is to be applied via the water, then it is important that the water is not blown through the solid constituents of the mix; experience shows that water is relatively easily pushed through particles larger than about 600 μm (No. 25) in diameter and is substantially held by particles smaller than this.

(3) In the same way, the mixture of cement, water and very fine aggregate particles should not be blown through the voids in the coarse aggregate. This can be achieved by ensuring that the aggregate grading does not have a complete absence of material in two consecutive sieve sizes – for example, between 10 mm (3/8 in.) and 2.36 mm (No. 7). In effect, any size of particle must act as a filter to prevent excessive movement of the next smaller size of material.

(4) Once it is established that the concrete can transmit pressure via the water in the mix without loss of the water, the resistance to the flow of the concrete through the pipeline should be reduced to a value which does not stop movement of the concrete, and preferably to a lower value which would reduce the consumption of power and the wear on the pipeline and increase the length of pipeline through which the concrete can be pumped. The resistance to flow is due primarily to friction between the concrete and the pipeline. This friction can be reduced by using concrete of a reasonably high workability, though too high a workability might make pumping more difficult in the light of points 2 and 3 above. Friction can also be reduced by reducing the total amount of fine materials and paricularly the fine aggregate in the concrete.

(5) The proportion of fine aggregate in a continuous overall grading of aggregate can be reduced in a number of ways. The maximum size of the aggregate can be made as large as possible; in practice, the maximum size in a 100 mm (4 in.) diameter pipeline is 20 mm (¾ in.), whereas in a 150 mm (6 in.) diameter pipeline a maximum aggregate size of 40 mm (1½ in.) can often be used. The coarse aggregate particle shape should be as round as possible; this means avoiding aggregates containing a high proportion of flaky or elongated particles. An apparatus, developed for measuring the voids content in coarse aggregate[79], can be used to assess the proportions of finer aggregate which would be needed with different types, sizes and gradings of coarser aggregate. Variations in particle shape at one particular sieve size can be detected and a compensation made, where a study of grading alone would not reveal problems with particle packing.

These considerations have several important effects on the properties of concrete for pumping. Firstly, the workability of the concrete cannot be varied widely and will, in general, have an average slump of between 50 and 100 mm (2 and 4 in.); the variation in workability must not be large — the slump would generally have to be within ±25 mm (1 in.) of the average value. Secondly, different types of pump and different lengths of pipeline will make different demands on the concrete and particularly on its workability; thus full-scale trials with the facility for modifying materials and proportions are essential. Thirdly, there are some types and gradings of aggregate which cannot economically be pumped, even though a carefully selected admixture may prove advantageous to materials of marginal quality (see later).

The process of selecting constituent materials and mix proportions should therefore be started in the normal manner discussed in this book, but care should be taken regarding the following points. The types of cement most usually used are ordinary Portland and sulphate-resisting Portland. Uniformity of aggregate supplies is very important — more important than in most other applications of concrete. Coarse aggregate of a very bad particle shape should be avoided. A grading in which there is a complete absence of material in two consecutive sieve sizes should be avoided: to put this another way, the object should be to ensure that there is always 1 or 2% of material retained on each of the test sieves normally used. The fine aggregate should contain a substantial proportion between the 600 μm (No. 25) and 300 μm (No. 52) sieves so as to provide good water-retention properties in the concrete. The proportion of fine aggregate below a 150 μm (No. 100) sieve should generally be kept to about 3% by weight of fine aggregate, since lower proportions might lead to a separation of aggregate and cement paste during pumping and larger proportions would be liable to increase the friction between the concrete and the pipeline; an exception occurs with concretes of very low cement content, where larger amounts might be an advantage. These requirements for the grading of the fine aggregate are not consistent with the gradings usually found with crushed materials, which are liable to contain too much material between the 5 mm (3/16 in.) and 2.36 mm (No. 7) sieves, too little between the 600 μm (No. 25) and 300 μm (No. 52) sieves and too much below the 150 μm (No. 100) sieve.

The proportions of fine aggregate to total aggregate should be kept as low as is reasonably consistent with other requirements of cohesiveness and of there being enough fine material to fill the voids in the coarse aggregate. In practice, the proportion of fine aggregate will usually be between 0 and 4% above the optimum sand content for conventionally placed mixes as discussed in Chapter 4. Generally, concretes which either segregate or bleed under normal conditions will not be suitable for pumping.

Concretes without admixtures and of high cement content, over about 450 kg/m³ (760 lb/yd³), are liable to prove difficult to pump because of high friction between the concrete and the pipeline. Cement contents below 270 to 320 kg/m³ (450 to 540 lb/yd³), depending upon the proportion of the aggregate, may also prove difficult to pump because of segregation within the pipeline.

Some types of lightweight aggregate are pumpable, whereas others are not. Materials easier in this respect are those which have a high proportion of sealed pores on their surface and are therefore comparatively unaffected by the increase of pressure experienced in a pipeline, whereas some porous materials, even if they are largely saturated with water before mixing, tend to take in some of the mixing water in the concrete, so lowering the amount of free water to an unacceptable extent.

Several types of admixture have proved beneficial in the pumping of concrete; for example, concretes of a wider range of cement content may prove pumpable. Air-entraining admixtures can sometimes improve those aspects of workability which reduce the pressure necessary in the pipeline. Air contents up to about 5% have been used; higher air contents and long lengths of pipeline are not suitable, as the compression of the air may reduce workability to an unacceptable extent or could absorb the movement of the piston so that little or no pumping would take place.

Admixtures of the surface-active and water-reducing types have been used beneficially with mixes producing a high friction in the pipeline. They are not so likely to be beneficial if the concrete is liable to segregate, and may even prove a disadvantage. Since high pipeline friction is often associated with mixes having a high proportion of fine material, a reduction in the proportion of fine to total aggregate might prove better than the use of the admixture. The potentially most useful admixtures are those which tend to reduce bleeding and segregation, as they reduce the tendency of the water to percolate through the solid particles. They also tend, however, to increase pipeline friction, though this can sometimes be offset by modifications to the materials or proportions. Admixtures based on polymers with long molecular chains such as polyethylene oxide, cellulose ethers and alginates have been used, though the widespread use of these materials is hindered by a lack of knowledge of the side effects.

The addition of finely divided powders such as bentonite or pulverized fuel ash has proved useful, particularly in very lean concretes.

6.24 Underwater concreting

Concrete which is to be placed under water by tremie or bottom-opening skip must have an exceptionally high workability − an average slump of 125 to 150 mm (5 to 6 in.) is generally used − so that, when placed in position, it will compact under its own weight which is effectively reduced in the buoyant conditions under water. It is unlikely to stand at an angle of greater than 5° to the horizontal in normal circumstances. No compactive effort can be applied, apart from light screeding by a diver, as this would be likely to mix further water with the concrete and so reduce its strength.

The maximum size of aggregate is generally 20 to 40 mm (¾ to 1½ in.); larger sizes are difficult to screed and may cause arching in the pipe if a tremie is being used. The concrete should be very cohesive; flaky or elongated coarse aggregate particles should be avoided and a relatively high proportion of fine aggregate used. Crushed rock fine aggregate may also prove unsuitable.

Due to the possible washing out of cement from the fresh concrete, it is usual to use 25% more cement than would otherwise be thought necessary. The cement content would not generally be less than 330 kg/m³ (560 lb/yd³), even though minimum compressive strengths over 25 N/mm² (3600 lbf/in²) at 28 days are generally avoided.

Bagged concrete has been used for much underwater work, though it is generally confined to temporary work. The concrete is mixed with water before being placed in the bags, which are then trodden into place by a diver. Large maximum sizes of aggregate should be avoided and the proportion of fine aggregate should be high, so as to obtain a very plastic, cohesive mix which can be easily remoulded in the bag.

6.25 Grouted concrete

Grouted or pre-packed concrete, in which a large-size coarse aggregate is placed and tamped in position and the voids are then grouted, is used in a number of special applications, including underwater concreting.

The coarse aggregate should have as large a maximum size as possible and should be graded down so that not more than 10% passes the 37.5 mm (1½ in.) sieve. This minimum size is the smallest that can reasonably be grouted without a likelihood of excessive air being trapped. The larger the maximum size of aggregate and the better the particle shape, the lower is the proportion of voids within the coarse aggregate and therefore the lower the quantity of grout per unit volume of completed concrete.

One of the most important aspects of the coarse aggregate is that it should be free from dirt and coatings since these would greatly impair the bond with the cement paste; this is more important in grouted concrete than in normally mixed concrete, where the action of mixing will often remove dirt from the coarse aggregate and mix it harmlessly into the cement paste.

The fine aggregate in the grout should have a maximum particle size of about one-eighth of the nominal minimum size of the coarse aggregate, so that the freshly mixed grout can pass easily through the voids in the coarse aggregate. The workability of the grout will be fixed by the nature of the grout mixer and the fact that the grout must penetrate the voids. The proportion of cement to fine aggregate will be raised to suit the required strength of the concrete, though it is unusual to aim for high strength with grouted concrete; a proportion of 1:2 of cement : dry fine aggregate and a water/cement ratio of about 0.5 are often used.

Many types of admixture have been used sucessfully in the grout, including pulverized-fuel ash and water-reducing admixtures. The former often replaces some of the cement where strength is unimportant, and the latter aims to improve the workability of the grout, often by reducing bleeding. Expanding agents are sometimes useful in causing the grout to expand slightly by releasing a gas while still plastic and so helping to fill the voids.

Proprietary aids to intrusion can help to keep the fine aggregate in suspension in the grout, to reduce bleeding of mixing water and to produce a colloidal effect.

6.26 Compaction by water extraction techniques

Production techniques involving the removal of part of the mixing water from the concrete after it has been placed are widely adopted in the precast concrete industry and sometimes in in-situ work. The main advantages are that a high-workability concrete can be placed relatively inexpensively, the final product has a considerably lower water/cement atio and can therefore be of high strength and good durability, and the freshly processed product can be stripped of its side moulds and left on a pallet to harden. The side moulds can therefore be used again almost immediately, so reducing the number of moulds needed. The principal examples of water extraction techniques are the hydraulic pressing of kerbs and paving flags and the spinning of lamp standards and pipes. Vacuum processing to remove water has also been used.

In this type of work it is not possible to process a test cube in the same way as the full-scale unit, and mix design in the conventional sense is quite impracticable. Further, the proportion of water remaining after processing probably varies through the thickness of the concrete, leading to variable quality; fortunately the surface of the concrete is likely to have the lower water/cement ratio and so will tend to have a higher strength and better durability.

The method of mix design for this type of work is therefore essentially one of trial and error. Several principles can, however, be kept in mind. During processing, the concrete will be subject to a pressure under which water will escape either through a special part of the mould (in pressing and vacuum work) or into the centre of a spun unit. Although the special moulds are designed so that cement does not escape, it is clearly desirable that, under the action of the pressure, cement is not removed from the fine aggregate nor the fine aggregate from the coarse aggregate; the position is very similar to point 3 of the discussion of concrete for pumping in Chapter 6.23. it therefore seems appropriate that the concrete for water extraction processes should, so far as is possible, be continuously graded, though clearly the point is not so important as with concrete for pumping.

The maximum size of aggregate is often quite small, particularly for hydraulic pressing, as this has the advantage of reducing the likely variation of the concrete within the cast units. It also helps to provide a cohesive concrete not so susceptible to segregation when being handled before processing. The proportion of very fine aggregate particles —below, say, a $600\,\mu m$ (No. 25) sieve — must be sufficient to avoid excessive segregation but, on the other hand, must not be so high as to reduce the rate at which the water can escape during processing; this latter point has some relation to point 2 in Chapter 6.23, though a contrary conclusion is drawn.

Crushed coarse and fine aggregates are often used for hydraulic pressing, partly because the unit has a better green strength on removal of the mould than would a concrete having an aggregate of more rounded particle shape.

CHAPTER 7

Calculations, trials and adjustment of mix proportions during production

7.1 General

Once an estimate of the likely mix proportions has been made, either from consideration of Chapters 4, 5 and 6 or from past experience, some calculations and trials will inevitably be needed before construction work can start. The particular stages needed will depend upon the circumstances, though for the purposes of this Chapter it is assumed that no past data exist and the selection of mix proportions has been based upon published data and upon an assessment of the required workability and type of aggregate to be used. The stages of work will then be:

(1) a determination of the grading of each size of aggregate to be used;

(2) a calculation of the proportions of each size of aggregate needed to reproduce the overall grading required;

(3) the calculation of batch quantities required for laboratory trial mixes, the preparation of the aggregate and the completion of the trial mix(es) and concrete tests;

(4) the probable adjustment of the mix proportions so as to meet more closely the required concrete properties;

(5) the making of one or more full-scale site trials.

7.2 Calculation of combined grading

Whatever the grading of the aggregate used in the mix design data (see, for example, Figures 4.3 to 4.5), it is extremely unlikely that the aggregates being used, even if obtained in several sizes and then combined on batching, will reproduce the type grading more than approximately. Three methods of calculation are given, each of which will provide a reasonable approximation depending upon the number of aggregates being combined and the gradings of each. Method 1 below is appropriate to as many sizes of aggregate as required, provided each size is substantially different: for example, aggregates of nominal sizes 20 to 10 mm (¾ to 3/8 in.), 10 to 5 mm (3/8 to 3/16 in.) and fine material below 5 mm (3/16 in.). Method 2 is for combining two sizes of aggregate, often where the sizes of the two materials are largely overlapping — for example, combining a very coarse sand with a fine sand to produce a more acceptable concreting sand. Method 3 is for combining two substantially different sizes, as might occur with a gapped grading using, for example, 20 to 10 mm (¾ to 3/8 in.) coarse aggregate and a fine aggregate.

Whichever method is used, it is important to ensure that the resulting combined grading provides sufficient mortar to fill the voids in the coarse aggregate when the concrete has been compacted. For example, in a grading of 20 mm (¾ in.) maximum size it is not usually advisable to use less than 25% of fine aggregate. If the calculation results in too low a value, it may be necessary to change the nominal sizes of aggregate used or to use a higher proportion of fine aggregate than is indicated; in either case, the mix proportions of the concrete may have to be re-assessed.

The grading of each size of aggregate must first be determined from a representative sample in accordance with BS 812. The sample of aggregate is best collected from the source of supply; if an inspection of the source suggests that the grading may differ substantially during production, it would be advisable to collect several samples at intervals so that the likely effect of the variation on the concrete may be estimated.

The results of these determinations all assume that the different sizes of aggregate being combined have similar specific gravities. Whilst differences in the specific gravity of natural dense aggregates are not likely to be significant, care must be exercised when different sizes of lightweight aggregate, or a lightweight coarse aggregate with a dense fine aggregate, are combined. In these instances the percentage of each size of aggregate, determined by any of the following three methods, should be multiplied by its specific gravity to give the relative proportion by weight (no longer the percentage) of each size of aggregate to be used in the trial mix.

7.2.1 Method 1[79]

This method is illustrated in Figure 7.1. The vertical scale of percentage passing is drawn on graph paper, together with the straight line a − h at any convenient slope. Vertical lines are then drawn through points on the line a − h corresponding to the values of the percentage of material intended to pass different sieves according to the required grading. These lines represent each of the sieve sizes, which are then marked on the horizontal scale.

The actual known gradings of each size of aggregate to be used are then plotted on the appropriate ordinates and the straight lines I, II, III are drawn to the steepest reasonable slope (that is, for preference, the steepest slope between about 10% and 90% passing). Straight lines are then drawn from the top of line I to the bottom of line II and from the top of line II to the bottom of line III. Where these lines, designated AB and CD, cut the original line a — h the points of intersection correspond to the proportions of each size of material needed to approximate as nearly as possible to the required grading.

In the example, which is a continuation of the example started in Chapter 4.4.4, the values are 38% and 60%; therefore the proportion of fine aggregate is 38%, that of 10 to 5 mm (3/8 to 3/16 in.) material is 60 − 38 = 22%, and that of 20 to 10 mm (¾ to 3/8 in.) material is 100 − 60 = 40%. The results obtained should be checked arithmetically, as in Table 7.1.

7.2.2 Method 2[1]

The second method is illustrated in Figure 7.2, where two sources of fine aggregate, referred to as material 1 and material 2, are to be combined. For the sake of an example, material 1 can be taken as a relatively inexpensive but very coarsely graded material just falling within grading zone 1 of BS 882. It is assumed that experience has shown that, for the particular work to be carried out, the fine aggregate grading should be no coarser than the coarser limit of zone 2. This material must therefore be combined with a more finely graded material which happens to be relatively

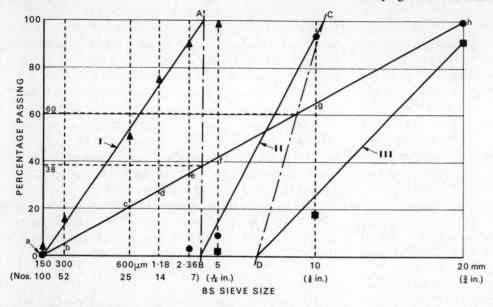

Figure 7.1 : Example of combined grading, using method 1.

TABLE 7.1
Calculation of combined grading (method 1).

	Aggregate	Sieve size								
		150 μm (No. 100)	300 μm (No. 52)	600 μm (No. 25)	1.18 mm (No. 14)	2.36 mm (No. 7)	5 mm (3/16 in.)	10 mm (3/8 in.)	20 mm (¾ in.)	37.5 mm (1½ in.)
Required grading (percentage passing)		0	5	21	28	35	42	65	100	100
Percentage of given aggregate passing sieve	Fine aggregate	2	16	51	75	90	99	100	100	100
	10 to 5 mm (3/8 to 3/16 in.)					3	9	94	100	100
	20 to 10 mm (¾ to 3/8 in.)						2	18	92	100
Required proportions of given aggregates	38% of fine aggregate	1	6	19	28	34	38	38	38	38
	22% of 10 to 5 mm (3/8 to 3/16 in.)					1	2	21	22	22
	40% of 20 to 10 mm (¾ to 3/8 in.)						1	7	37	40
Combined grading (percentage passing)		1	6	19	28	35	41	66	97	100

expensive and to fall within zone 3. Clearly as high a proportion of material 1 as possible should be used to produce the most economical concrete. The gradings used are given in Table 7.2.

Referring to Figure 7.2, for each sieve size the percentage passing is marked on the left-hand ordinate representing material 1 and similarly on the right-hand ordinate representing material 2; lines are then drawn between these ordinates. On these lines can be marked the coarser limits of zone 2, and these points can be joined as shown by the broken line. Now, referring to the horizontal scale, the effect of any particular percentage of material 1 in the mixture of the two materials can be examined: the grading of that combined material is given by the corresponding vertical line where it crosses the various sieve sizes. If any part of the vertical line falls to the left of the broken line, the grading of the combined material will not meet the original requirement that the grading of the combined

material should not be coarser than zone 2. From the example it can be seen that any proportion of materials up to 70% of material 1 will meet the requirement, and since material 1 is the cheaper the proportion to select *is* 70%. The grading of the combined material can be read off and is given in Table 7.2.

This method of combination can also be used to avoid excessively fine gradings, or possibly to check that the combination of two materials falls within a required grading range — for example, Figure 6.4, 6.5 or 6.15.

7.2.3   Method 3 [80]

This method, often called an arithmetical method, is based on the principle that concretes of similar aggregate/cement and water/cement ratios and similar maximum size and type of aggregate will have similar workabilities, provided

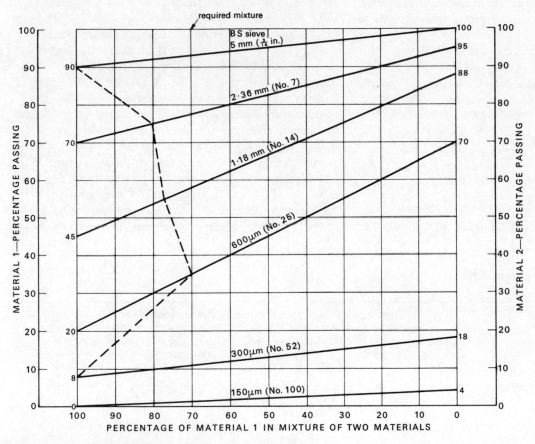

Figure 7.2 : Example of combined grading, using method 2.

TABLE 7.2
Calculation of combined grading (method 2).

Sieve size	Percentage passing			
	Material 1	Material 2	Coarser limit to zone 2	Combined grading
5 mm (3/16 in.)	90	100	90	93
2.36 mm (No. 7)	70	95	75	78
1.18 mm (No. 14)	45	88	55	58
600 μm (No. 25)	20	70	35	35
300 μm (No. 52)	8	18	8	11
150 μm (No. 100)	0	4	0	1

the total specific surface of all the aggregate particles in each mix is the same, even though the grading of the aggregate may be substantially different. To avoid having to measure the specific surface of each size of aggregate, an arbitrary surface area index is used, in which the index is doubled each time the aggregate size is halved. In effect this is equivalent to assuming that the particle shape of the aggregate does not change from one size to the next. The theory breaks down at very small sizes, so the same index is used for all material below a 300 μm (No. 52) sieve size.

An example of the calculation is shown in Table 7.3. The last three columns are completed by cross-multiplying the grading required, and the grading of the coarse and fine aggregates separately, by the surface area index. These last three columns are then summed and divided by 100 to give the surface area index for that particular grading. The surface area indices of the coarse and fine materials are then combined in such a proportion as to give a combined surface area index the same as that of the required grading. That is, if a represents the proportion of fine aggregate to total aggregate, then

$$1.5 (100 - a) + 55.0 \, a = 16.8 \times 100$$
$$\therefore a = 29\%$$

This method can be extended to three sizes by initially assuming that single-size coarse aggregates — for example, 20 to 10 mm (¾ to 3/8 in.) and 10 to 5 mm (3/8 to 3/16 in.) material — would be combined in the ratio 2 : 1 by weight.

7.3 Batch weights and yields

It is often necessary to calculate the batch weights of concrete with the object of determining the quantities of constituent materials, either to make enough concrete for a trial mix or to fill a certain mixer economically.

The quantity of concrete needed in a trial mix is usually taken as at least 10% more than the quantity strictly needed for the tests to be carried out. A certain amount of re-use of fresh concrete is permissible if the testing is carried out quickly; for example, concrete used for a slump test can be re-used for the compacting factor test. Exceptions occur with air-entrained concrete and concrete made with highly absorptive aggregate, for example lightweight aggregate, where all tests should be carried out as quickly as possible without any re-use of the concrete.

Assume that the trial mix for the example started in Chapter 4.4.4 required a total of 50 kg (110 lb) of concrete. The quantity of cement required can be simply calculated by dividing the 50 kg (110 lb) by the sum of the aggregate/cement ratio by weight, the water/cement ratio and one; that is, $50 \div (4.4 + 0.5 + 1) =$ about 8.5 kg (18.75 lb). The quantity of aggregate is then 4.4 x 8.5 = 37.4 kg (82.5 lb), which can be split as follows: 40% or 15.0 kg (33.1 lb) of 20 to 10 mm (¾ to 3/8 in.) aggregate; 22% or 8.2 kg (18.1 lb) of 10 to 5 mm (3/8 to 3/16 in.) aggregate; and 38% or 14.2 kg (31.2 lb) of fine aggregate. The quantity of water is 4.25 kg (9.4 lb), based on the aggregate being in a saturated, surface-dry condition.

Alternatively, it may be necessary to produce a full load of concrete from a mixer, the capacity of which is usually quoted in m^3 or in litres (yd^3 or ft^3). If aggregates of normal density are assumed, the weight of concrete in kg (lb) can be determined by multiplying the capacity of the mixer in m^3 (ft^3) by 2350 kg/m^3 (150 lb/ft^3), which can be taken, in the absence of more accurate data, as being the normal density of fresh concrete. If the capacity is

TABLE 7.3
Calculation of combined grading (method 3).

Range of aggregate (sieve size)	Surface area index	Grading (percentage between sieves)			Surface area indices		
		Required	Available aggregates		Required	Available aggregates	
			Fine	Coarse		Fine	Coarse
37.5 to 20 mm (1½ to ¾ in.)	1	41	0	58	41	0	58
20 to 10 mm (¾ to 3/8 in.)	2	15	0	40	30	0	80
10 to 5 mm (3/8 to 3/16 in.)	4	12	0	2	48	0	8
5 to 2.36 mm (3/16 in. to No. 7)	8	7	3	0	56	24	0
2.36 to 1.18 mm (Nos. 7 to 14)	16	8	16	0	128	256	0
1.18 mm to 600 μm (Nos. 14 to 25)	32	5	23	0	160	736	0
600 to 300 μm (Nos. 25 to 52)	64	5	46	0	320	2944	0
passing 300 μm (No. 52)	128	7	12	0	896	1536	0
			Total		1679	5496	146
			Surface area index		16.8	55.0	1.5

Note: The fact that successive metric sizes are not exactly in the ratio 2 : 1 is not of practical significance in this calculation.

expressed in litres, this quantity should be multiplied by 2.35, which again gives the weight of concrete in kg. Once the weight of concrete has been found, the batch weight can be determined in the same way as in the previous paragraph.

On a site where a comparatively large mixer is used the same procedures would apply, with the added refinement that the weights of aggregate may be increased by typical moisture contents which might well be taken as 2% and 6% for coarse and fine aggregates respectively. When this has been done, it is usual to round off all the batch weights to the nearest 5 kg (10 lb).

A further value, often required for estimation purposes, is the yield from a batch of concrete. This can be determined in two ways. A reasonable approximation is to divide the total weight of the constituents (including the water) in kg (lb) by 2350 kg/m^3 (150 lb/ft^3) to give the volume of fully compacted fresh concrete in m^3 (ft^3). A more precise value would be obtained by using an experimentally determined density or by dividing the weight of each constituent by its specific gravity (using the dry weight in the case of the aggregate) and summing the numbers obtained, which would give the yield in litres; this value can then be changed to m^3 by dividing by 1000.

7.4 Trial mixes

7.4.1 Evidence of suitability of mix proportions

Evidence of the suitability of constituent materials and mix proportions should be obtained for all structural concrete well in advance of construction. The exception to this is when standard or prescribed mixes are to be used and the materials and proportions have been selected to give reasonable assurance that the resulting concrete will satisfy the requirements of the work in hand.

The evidence of suitability is most often obtained from past work, using the same sources of materials, mix proportions and general conditions of quality control. There are, however, other instances where full data are not available and must be supplemented by further work. The most important part of this work is the full-scale trial mix on site, using the same bulk materials, the same batching and mixing equipment and the same general procedure as will be used for the construction work; these trial mixes can then be followed, if necessary, by the casting of trial sections of the work. It is only by such full-scale trials that it is possible to ensure that the concrete can be mixed, transported and placed satisfactorily.

Site trials, however, suffer one considerable disadvantage: if, as is generally the case, strength tests are required, probably at an age of 28 days after casting, it is often uneconomic to set up the site plant sufficiently in advance of the actual construction to obtain the results. The best course of action in this instance, therefore, is to precede the site trials by laboratory trials. It is also wise to make trial mixes well in advance of the site work whenever the specification calls for concrete with properties outside the normal run of experience — for example, a concrete

required to have a particular flexural or indirect tensile strength, or a very high strength, or to contain a particular admixture.

7.4.2 Laboratory trial mixes

Laboratory trial mixes have considerable advantages over site trial mixes in that it is possible to ensure careful storage and accurate batching of materials, and thorough mixing of the concrete, under conditions where the temperature can be maintained reasonably constant (20 ± 5°C), and where the relative humidity can be maintained at over 50%. A further advantage is that the aggregate can be used in a known condition, either air-dry or saturated, so making possible a more accurate estimate of the water content of the concrete during mixing.

There are, however, a number of difficulties, which can be overcome relatively easily. It is likely that the original estimate of the required mix proportions will include the free water/cement ratio; if this is so, and the aggregates are air-dry, some allowance will have to made for the absorption of water by the aggregates. The amount of water absorbed can be calculated from a knowledge of the water absorption determined in accordance with subsection 4A of BS 812 : 1967 and of the oven-dry moisture determined in accordance with section 5 of this Standard. Alternatively, the original estimate of the mix proportions will have included the total water/cement ratio, in which case all the water added at the mixer can be considered as being a part of the water/cement ratio. (Strictly speaking, this can introduce small errors, but these can generally be ignored.) Whichever way the quantity of water required is assessed, the use of air-dry aggregate inevitably means that water will be absorbed by the aggregates, more particularly in the first few minutes after mixing. It is therefore advisable to leave the concrete to stand in the mixer for about 15 minutes after the completion of initial mixing; the concrete should be covered by a damp cloth to reduce evaporation during this time. At the end of this period most of the absorption will have taken place and the concrete should be briefly re-mixed, after which measurements of workability and strength will be more reliable.

An alternative procedure is to use the aggregate in a saturated condition by pre-soaking. This has the advantage that absorption of water by the aggregates during and after mixing does not occur. The aggregate should be batched in an air-dry condition and a predetermined quantity of water added so that, provided evaporation is reduced to a minimum, the total moisture content of the aggregate can be determined reasonably accurately or, with the aid of data on the water absorption of the aggregate, the free moisture content can be calculated. Any doubts regarding the correct quantity of mixing water to add can often be overcome not by trying to add the estimated quantity exactly but by adding sufficient water to make concrete of the required workability. If the original estimate of required water were to be seriously different from that actually used, this would be shown by simple calculation of the added water/cement ratio even if an accurate value for absorption were not available.

Details of making and testing laboratory trial mixes are given in BS 1881 : 1970. The number and range of tests made on the mixed concrete will depend upon the requirements of the particular mix. Strength determinations should be made from at least three test specimens at any one age, and workability tests should be duplicated — if the two results do not show good agreement a third test should be done.

Specimens are usually taken for test at an age of 28 days, though it is often advisable to take further specimens for test at earlier ages such as 1, 3 or 7 days, as this would provide useful data if ever subsequent work showed that some change in mix proportions was necessary. Early-age results also enable an estimate of the relation between these and the 28-day results to be made, so that early-age results might be used on site as a means of obtaining an early estimate of the 28-day strength.

Further, if the quality control procedures intended for the full-scale work involve accelerated curing tests or indeed any other form of rapid test, these should also be carried out at the trial mix stage so as to obtain a correlation between the accelerated test value and the specified strength.

One important aspect of making trial mixes is to observe the behaviour of the concrete as it is being mixed, handled and compacted. The suitability of the workability for the work should be kept in mind, the cohesiveness and stability of the mix should be judged and the tendency to segregation or bleeding noted. The amount of compactive effort applied to the concrete test specimens is liable to be considerably greater than that which will be applied during construction, so it is important not to underestimate the workability which will be needed on site (see Chapter 4.3). The ease of trowelling the surface of test specimens often provides a guide to the ease with which the final work can be finished.

The density of the fresh concrete should also be determined, as it is from this value that the cement content of the concrete can be determined and compared with, for example, any limiting values of cement content specified to meet specific durability requirements.

As an illustration of this point, the example started in Chapter 4.4.4 and continued in Chapter 7.2.1 can be further continued. Suppose the density of the fresh concrete has been determined as 2350 kg/m³ (148 lb/ft³). The cement content is found by dividing the fresh density by the sum of the aggregate/cement ratio by weight, the water/cement ratio and one to represent the cement, that is,

$$\frac{2350}{4.4 + 0.50 + 1} = 400 \text{ kg/m}^3 \ (680 \text{ lb/yd}^3)$$

This is greater than the minimum cement content required to meet the durability requirements, and no change in mix proportions is necessary to satisfy this point.

For important work it is advisable not to rely upon the results of one trial mix but to make two or three so that any accidental errors will not adversely affect the final work. Although a repetition of the first trial mix will undoubtedly be useful, considerably greater benefit can usually be obtained by making the second and subsequent trial mix proportions slightly different, preferably by changing the richness of the mix and aiming for the same workability as the original mix. For example, if the original trial mix had an aggregate/cement ratio of 5.5 by weight, the next two mixes should have aggregate/cement ratios of 5 and 6 or even of 4.5 and 6.5. The advantage of such a procedure is that, if the strength of the first trial mix were unacceptably different from the target mean strength, the adjustment of mix proportions would be made much easier. An advantage might also be noted during the actual construction work, where some contingency might require a change in the mix proportions and such a change could more reliably be made on the basis of the greater amount of trial data available. The making of several trial mixes also means that the original estimate of mix proportions need not be very precise; indeed the making of one or two extra trial mixes is probably more valuable to the satisfactory completion of the construction work than a complex and very precise estimate of mix proportions in the first instance.

When trial mixes of air-entrained concrete are made, it is preferable that the aggregates should be saturated before mixing because air expelled from the aggregate during absorption of mixing water might lead to a false estimate of air content. The admixture should be mixed with a relatively high proportion of the mixing water before being added to the aggregates, so as to obtain the best distribution of the admixture through the mix. Machine mixing should be adopted.

Trial mixes of lightweight aggregate concrete require careful consideration from two points of view. Firstly, the water absorption of the aggregate is likely to be high and it is probable that several properties of the concrete — for example, the density of the fresh concrete — will be significantly affected by the amount of absorption which has taken place. Every attempt should therefore be made to see that the aggregates used for the laboratory trials are in as similar a condition as possible to those which will be used for the actual construction. Secondly, it should be noted that many laboratory mixers rely on a forced action which might break up the weaker coarse aggregate particles, so giving misleading results.

7.4.3 Interpretation of laboratory trial mix results

Keeping in mind that the mix proportions used for the trial mixes are at best an estimate of the proportions needed for the work, it is likely that some adjustment to these estimates will be needed before construction work can start.

The test results should firstly be examined from the point of view of variation within themselves. For example, if two nominally similar mixes give significantly different results, then one or other — or both — are liable to be wrong. If time is available, the mixes should be repeated. More often time is not available, and the likely source of error should be examined and the mix proportions used for the work should be decided in such a way as to ensure a satisfactory structure, if necessary at the expense of economy. The range of strength results from three specimens from a single batch should not exceed 15% of their average strength, and the range of three batch averages should not exceed 20% of the average for all the batches. If results fall outside these ranges, then the testing procedure should be examined. If the trial mixes are of different proportions this latter check can clearly not be applied, but it is usually possible to judge with the aid of mix design data, for example the data described in Chapter 4, whether or not the test results of one mix are consistent with those of another.

Once the test results are judged to be reasonable, the results should be compared with the original requirements for strength, workability and possibly such factors as air content and fresh density. Any gross errors associated with workability, air content or fresh density will have been noted at the time the trial mix was made and, if necessary, a modified mix will have been made, so the only factor still requiring consideration will generally be the strength. If compressive strength is within about 5 N/mm^2 (750 lbf/in^2) of the target mean strength, it is usual to accept the mix proportions and to proceed with full-scale work, though it is often quite easy to make a fine adjustment to the proportions by referring to the mix design data used for the original estimate. If the compressive strength is between 5 and 10 N/mm^2 (750 and 1500 lbf/in^2) of the required target value, then, subject to the requirements of the specification, some adjustment should be made. If the trial mix strength is more than about 10 N/mm^2 (1500 lbf/in^2) lower than the target, then some more fundamental error has probably been made, possibly in the choice of the original constituents or the selection of proportions, and the mix design should be reconsidered.

Continuing the example started in Chapter 4.4.4 and continued in Chapters 7.2.1 and 7.3, if the trial mix compressive strength is 43.5 N/mm^2 (6300 lbf/in^2) instead of 40 N/mm^2 (5800 lbf/in^2) an examination of Figure 4.2 will show that the difference between the two strengths is equivalent to a difference in water/cement ratio of 0.04. According to Table 4.7 this change in water/cement ratio is equivalent to a change in aggregate/cement ratio of 0.4 for the same grading of aggregate and workability of concrete; thus construction work should proceed using an aggregate/ cement ratio numerically 0.4 higher than the original estimate, i.e. 4.8, provided the revised cement content is still above the specified minimum, which it is (as is evident from Figure 2.1) — 370 kg/m^3 as against 360 kg/m^3, or 625 lb/yd^3 as against 605 lb/yd^3.

It is useful, particularly in the case of high-strength concrete, to have a knowledge of the rate of gain of strength of the cement used in the trial mixes in relation to the rate of gain generally experienced with that particular source of cement. Clearly, if the cement used in the trial mixes has a higher rate of gain than that generally experienced it would be unwise to reduce the proportion of cement in the mix because of a slightly high trial result; on the other hand, low results would be regarded more seriously in this instance than if the cement were more typical.

7.4.4 Full-scale trial mixes

Trial mixes should always be made under full-scale site conditions for any work of any importance, whether or not laboratory trials have been made. Site trials should follow as closely as possible the proposed procedure for the rest of the work, except that the test batch produced will be used for rather more tests than usual and the rest of the concrete should not be used in any important part of the structure.

Before the trials take place, the batching and mixing plant should be set up and checked for good mechanical working order, and the batching devices for cement, aggregates and water should be checked and, if possible, calibrated. The aggregates used are likely to be wet, and a knowledge of the moisture content will be needed to check whether or not the water/cement ratio of the concrete is correct. Even if the moisture content is not known, the concrete should be mixed to the workability estimated as being required during the mix design or laboratory trials. In this way the need to make careful allowance for such finer points as the distinction between free and total water/cement ratio can be avoided; the strength and the workability of the concrete can be related directly.

Tests should not be made on the first batch of concrete out of the mixer as a high proportion of the cement paste will have coated the inside of the mixer, leaving the coarse aggregate with an unknown proportion of cement paste, even if the batch weight of coarse aggregate has been reduced arbitrarily to offset the loss of paste. The second, or preferably the third batch, which will be reasonably representative of the intended concrete, should be used for the trial tests. Apart from the obvious tests for strength and workability, and possibly for air content and fresh density, the following points should be noted:

(1) whether the total quantity of material is overloading the mixer;

(2) whether the concrete can be fully mixed within a reasonable time or whether the mix on discharge appears segregated (this could perhaps be rectified by a modified sequence of loading the mixer or batching hopper with the cement and various sizes of aggregates);

(3) whether the workability of the concrete is correct for the work intended, including such considerations as the method of transporting, placing and compacting (the original estimate of the workability may not prove correct and some hasty adjustments to mix proportions may be necessary — any such adjustments would be greatly eased if laboratory trial mix data are available).

So long as the trials are completed satisfactorily and the concrete, as produced on site, is the same or very similar to that made during the laboratory work, it is generally possible to proceed with construction work without waiting for strength tests, though a few early-age test results would add confidence to the start of full-scale work. An exception arises in the case of a target mean compressive 28-day strength above about 60 N/mm^2 (8500 lbf/in^2), when at least 7-day test results from site trials should be available; for target 28-day strengths of 80 N/mm^2 (11 500 lbf/in^2)

or more, it would be preferable to have the 28-day values themselves before work is started.

7.5 Routine adjustments to mix proportions during production

During the course of concrete production there are several inevitable changes in the properties of the constituent materials; these changes require some action on the part of those responsible for maintaining the correct overall properties of the concrete. These changes are in fact a routine part of good quality control. The principal example is the changing moisture content of the aggregates, which involves changes in the quantity of water needed to be added to maintain the correct workability; this leads, assuming accurate batching, to reasonable control over the water/cement ratio in the concrete. Another example is the need to adjust the workability of concrete which is to be transported over a considerable distance, to allow for the more rapid stiffening of the concrete in hot weather. The significant point about adjustments such as these is that they do not involve any change in the target values of the variable involved, such as strength, workability or air content.

A change in the grading of fine aggregate justifies special mention. The results of routine grading analyses will inevitably show the grading to be slightly different each time it is tested; some of the differences will truly represent a change in the grading and some will be largely due to variation in sampling and testing. Any really significant differences should in practice be offset by aiming to maintain a constant aggregate surface area and therefore by changing the proportion of fine aggregate to total aggregate. An assessment could be made by using the method given in Chapter 7.2.3. In practice, it is not often necessary to adopt such a procedure, and a change in the proportion of fine aggregate can be accepted as justified when the fine aggregate grading changes by the equivalent of a full grading zone as defined in BS 882; as the grading becomes finer, the proportion should be reduced.

The circumstances in which concrete is being placed may alter in the course of the work, and an adjustment to one target value may be justified without any other target value being changed. For example, a particularly congested section may require the use of concrete of a higher workability, yet no change to the compressive strength is permissible. The effect of any such change on the mix proportions can usually be estimated from the data in Chapter 4, even though the mix may not have been designed using these data. For example, with reference to Table 4.7, a mix having an aggregate/cement ratio of 4.8 and 'medium' workability would have the same water/cement ratio and therefore the same compressive strength as a mix of aggregate/cement ratio 4.4 having 'high' workability. Therefore the richer mix with the higher workability could safely be used for the congested section without significant effect on the strength of the concrete. Changes in the aggregate grading can be similarly determined.

The same principle can be applied to the compressive strength of concrete. If, for example, the average 28-day strength determined from a considerable number of routine tests was, say, 5 N/mm^2 (720 lbf/in^2) above the target mean value of 40 N/mm^2 (5800 lbf/in^2), it might be appropriate to adjust the mix proportions to aim more closely for the target value. Reference to Figure 4.2 shows that a change in water/cement ratio of 0.05 would bring about such a change. Reference would then be made to the appropriate table of aggregate/cement ratio for different types and maximum sizes of aggregate to determine the extent to which a change in aggregate/cement ratio might be brought about by such an increase in water/cement ratio. The numerical increases in both the water/cement and aggregate/cement ratios could then be applied to the job (subject to compliance with any specified minimum cement content), even though the actual values used on the job may have been altered at the trial mix stage from those originally found in the tables and graph.

Clearly it is not worth while adjusting mix proportions for every set of test results as they become available, because many of the differences from one set of test results to the next can be attributed to sampling and testing errors. However, as more test results become available, the more reliable any indication of a need to change mix proportions will become. The probability that test results are significantly higher or lower than the target mean strength can be assessed by using Figure 7.3. The four latest, or twenty latest, test results are averaged, and the amount by which the average is higher or lower than the target mean strength is expressed as a proportion of the standard deviation (either the known value or the one estimated as representing the degree of control being exercised on site — see Chapter 4.2). Using this proportion, and reading from the horizontal scale to the curve representing the number of test results being used, the probability that the concrete is really of higher or lower strength can be determined. In practice it is probably not worth while making any adjustment unless it is 95% certain that a real change has taken place. The curve for single specimens is also given in Figure 7.3, and this shows that a single result has to be well off target before a change is justified.

Although Figure 7.3 has been discussed in terms of compressive strength and, by implication, in terms of an age of test of 28 days, the principle can be applied to any parameter for which a target mean value and a standard deviation of routine test results are known. the other most likely examples would be an accelerated compressive strength test[42, 43] or the results of an analysis of fresh concrete[81, 82], both of which have the great advantage of providing data on the quality control being achieved in sufficient time for any necessary action to be taken before much further work has been completed. To utilize these procedures fully it is necessary to relate the results of the particular test procedure to the specified properties of the concrete, usually the 28-day strength. If the relation between the two is not good, it may be advisable to aim for a slightly higher margin over the specified strength in order that the early-age test results do not give a false impression of adequate quality control.

7.6 Change in strength margin during production

A change in the compressive strength margin (see Chapter 4.2) may become appropriate if the test results obtained during the course of the work show the margin to be consistently too high or too low because the anticipated standard deviation of test results was incorrect. Calculated standard deviations from limited numbers of test results will vary to some extent, even though the actual degree of control has not altered; such variations were discussed in Chapter 1 and are due largely to sampling and testing errors and to the inevitable limitation on the number of test results which can be obtained on site. A criterion by which it is possible to judge whether or not the measured standard deviation really differs from the initially assumed value is given in Figure 7.4. If the standard deviation determined from a sufficient number of test results, divided by the initially assumed standard deviation, falls outside the two curves drawn on the graph, then there is a 95% or more probability that the two values represent significantly different degrees of control. The higher the number of results available, the less do the two values need to differ for the difference to be significant; results based on less than about 40 results are not sufficiently reliable to justify ·accepting a change in the standard deviation. Any significantly changed standard deviation can then be multiplied by 1.64 to give the revised margin (see Chapter 4.2). The extent of any change in the mix proportions will depend on the change in the margin and the target mean strength; this can be estimated using mix design data in the same way as discussed in the previous section.

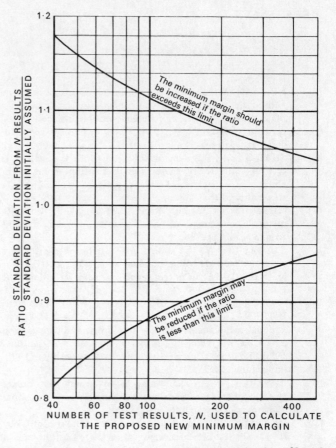

Figure 7.4 : Limits for the ratio $\dfrac{\text{standard deviation from } N \text{ results}}{\text{initially assumed standard deviation}}$

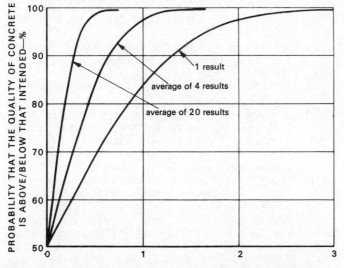

Figure 7.3 : Relation between actual quality and the probability that the concrete is really of higher or lower quality than intended.

REFERENCES

[1]   ROAD RESEARCH LABORATORY. Design of concrete mixes. Second edition. London, HMSO, 1950. pp.16. Road Note No. 4.

[2]   NEWMAN, A.J. and TEYCHENNÉ, D.C. A classification of natural sands and its use in concrete mix design. Proceedings of a symposium on mix design and quality control of concrete, London, May 1954. London, Cement and Concrete Association, 1955. pp.175-194.

[3]   SHACKLOCK, B.W. and WALKER, W.R. The specific surface of concrete aggregates and its relation to the workability of concrete. London, Cement and Concrete Association, July 1958. pp.9. Research Report 41.004.

[4]   MURDOCK, L.J. and BLACKLEDGE, G.F. Concrete materials and practice. Fourth edition. London, Edward Arnold, 1968. pp.398.

[5]   STEWART, D.A. The design and placing of high quality concrete. Second edition. London, Spon, 1962. pp.162.

[6]   McINTOSH, J.D. Concrete and statistics. London, CR Books, 1963. pp.139.

[7]   COMITÉ EUROPÉEN DU BÉTON – FÉDÉRATION INTERNATIONALE DE LA PRÉCONTRAINTE. International recommendations for the design and construction of concrete structures. FIP Sixth Congress, Prague, June 1970. London, Cement and Concrete Association, 1970. Publication 12.035.

[8]   ERNTROY, H.C. The variation of works test cubes. London, Cement and Concrete Association, November 1960. pp.28. Research Report 41.010.

[9]   METCALF, J.B. The specification of concrete strength. Part II: The distribution of strength of concrete for structures in current practice. Crowthorne, Road Research Laboratory, 1970. pp.22. RRL Report LR 300.

[10]   CEMENT AND CONCRETE ASSOCIATION. Notes on the specification for ready mixed concrete. London, December 1966. pp.8. Publication 45.006.

[11]   CEMENT AND CONCRETE ASSOCIATION. Notes on the specification of concrete mixes for housing estate roads. London, October 1969. pp.2. Publication 46.011.

[12]   LEA, F.M. The chemistry of cement and concrete. Third edition. London, Edward Arnold, 1970. pp.727.

[13]   DEPARTMENT OF THE ENVIRONMENT. Special cements. Fourth edition. London, HMSO, 1972. Advisory Leaflet 39.

[14]   BUILDING RESEARCH ESTABLISHMENT. Concrete: materials. Garston, February 1973. pp.7. Building Research Establishment Digest 150.

[15]   CEMENT AND CONCRETE ASSOCIATION. Impurities in aggregates for concrete. London, February 1970. pp.7. Publication 45.016.

[16]   CEMENT AND CONCRETE ASSOCIATION. An introduction to lightweight concrete. Fourth edition. London, 1970. pp.30. Publication 45.001.

[17]   SHORT, A. and KINNIBURGH, W. Lightweight concrete. Second edition. London, CR Books, 1968. pp.368.

[18]   TEYCHENNÉ, D.C. Lightweight aggregates: their properties and use in the United Kingdom. Proceedings of the first international congress on lightweight concrete, London, May 1968. London, Cement and Concrete Association, 1968. Vol. 1. Session A, Paper 3. pp.23-37. Publication 54.002.

[19]   BUILDING RESEARCH STATION. Lightweight aggregate concretes. Garston, November 1970. pp.4. Building Research Station Digest 123.

[20]   LYDON, F.D. and KEEN, R.A. Expanded polystyrene as a lightweight aggregate. London, Cement and Concrete Association, December 1966. pp.12. Departmental Note DN/1006.

[21]   RILEM-ABEM. Proceedings of an international symposium on admixtures for mortar and concrete, Brussels, 30 August – 1 September 1967.

[22]   AMERICAN CONCRETE INSTITUTE COMMITTEE 212. Admixtures for concrete. Journal of the American Concrete Institute. Proceedings Vol. 60, No. 11. November 1963. pp.1481-1526.

[23]   NETHERLANDS COMMITTEE FOR CONCRETE RESEARCH. Admixtures for concrete. Amsterdam, 1965. CUR Report 31. Published in English by the Cement and Concrete Association, London, August 1968. C&CA Library Translation 61.131.

[24]   THE CONCRETE SOCIETY. Admixtures for concrete. Report of the sub-committee on admixtures set up within The Concrete Society. London, December 1967. pp.12. Technical Report TRCS 1.

[25]   SHACKLOCK, B.W. Admixtures as an aid to concrete construction. The science of admixtures: proceedings of a symposium organized jointly by The Concrete Society and the Cement Admixtures Association, London, 6 November 1969. London, The Concrete Society, 1970. pp.7-19. Publication 54.004.

[26]   AMERICAN SOCIETY FOR TESTING AND MATERIALS. Symposium on effect of water-reducing admixtures and set-retarding admixtures on properties of concrete. 1959. pp.246. Special Technical Publication No. 266.

[27]   BRUERE, G.M. Importance of mixing sequence when using set-retarding agents with Portland cement. Nature. Vol. 199. 6 July 1963. pp.32-33.

[28]   DODSON, V.H. and FARKAS, E. Delayed addition of set-retarding admixtures to Portland cement concrete. ASTM Proceedings. Vol. 64. pp.816-826.

[29]   JAEGERMANN, C.H. and RAVINA, D. Effect of some admixtures on early shrinkage and other properties of prolonged-mixed concrete subject to high evaporation. Proceedings of an international symposium on admixtures for mortar and concrete, 30 August – 1 September 1967. RILEM-ABEM. Topic IV, Report 18. pp.319-350.

[30]   WARRIS, B. Effect of admixtures on the properties of fresh mortar and concrete. Matériaux et Constructions – Materials and Structures. Vol. 1, No. 2. March/April 1968. pp.97-114. Reproduced in: Proceedings of an international symposium on admixtures for mortar and concrete, 30 August – 1 September 1967. RILEM-ABEM. General Report to Topic III. pp.27-48.

[31]   SCHIDELER, J.J. Calcium chloride in concrete. Journal of the American Concrete Institute. Proceedings Vol. 48, No. 6. March 1952. pp.537-559.

[32]   CENTRAL ELECTRICITY GENERATING BOARD. Pfa utilization. London, 1972. pp.104.

[33]   KROONE, B. Carbon black as a pigment for concrete products. Commonwealth Scientific and Industrial Research Organization, Australia, 1966. pp. 10. Report T3-2.

[34]   KEMPSTER, E. Pumpable concrete. Garston, Building Research Station, August 1969. pp.14. Current Paper CP 29/69.

[35]   NEWMAN, K. Properties of concrete. Structural Concrete. Vol. 2, No. 11. September/October 1965. pp.451-482.

[36]   DEWAR, J.D. Relations between various workability control tests for ready-mixed concrete. London, Cement and Concrete Association, February 1964. pp.17. Technical Report 42.375.

[37]   ERNTROY, H.C. and SHACKLOCK, B.W. Design of high-strength concrete mixes. Symposium on mix design and quality control of concrete, London, May 1954. London, Cement and Concrete Association, 1955. pp.55-73. Discussion: pp.163-166.

[38]   PARROTT, L.J. The selection of constituents and proportions for producing workable concrete with a compressive cube strength of 80 to 110 N/mm² (11 600 to 15 900 lbf/in²). London, Cement and Concrete Association, May 1969. pp.12. Technical Report 42.416.

[39]   PARROTT, L.J. The properties of high-strength concrete. London, Cement and Concrete Association, May 1969. pp.13. Technical Report 42.417.

[40] LAWRENCE, C.D. The properties of cement paste compacted under high pressure. London, Cement and Concrete Association, 1969. pp.21. Research Report 41.019.

[41] OWENS, P.L. Private communication.

[42] INSTITUTION OF CIVIL ENGINEERS ACCELERATED TESTING COMMITTEE. An accelerated test for concrete. Proceedings of the Institution of Civil Engineers. Vol. 40, May 1968, pp.125-133; Vol. 41, October 1968, pp.387-388; Vol. 45, March 1970, pp.535-541.

[43] GRANT, N.T. The use of an accelerated testing method in the quality control of ready mixed concrete. Proceedings of a symposium on concrete quality, London, November 1964. London, Cement and 'Concrete Association, 1966. pp.172-180. Publication 21.008.

[44] POWERS, T.C., COPELAND, L.E., HAYES, J.C. and MANN, H.M. Permeability of Portland cement paste. Journal of the American Concrete Institute. Proceedings Vol. 51, No. 3. November 1954. pp.285-298.

[45] POWERS, T.C., COPELAND, L.E. and MANN, H.M. Capillary continuity or discontinuity in cement pastes. Journal of the PCA Research and Development Labortories. Vol. 1, No. 2. May 1959. pp.38-48.

[46] BUILDING RESEARCH STATION. The durability of reinforced concrete in buildings. London, HMSO, 1956. pp.27. National Building Studies Special Report No. 25.

[47] BUILDING RESEARCH STATION. Protection against corrosion of reinforcing steel in concrete. Garston, June 1965. pp.8. Building Research Station Digest 59 (second series).

[48] BUILDING RESEARCH STATION. Concrete in sulphate-bearing soils and groundwaters. Garston, February 1968 (minor revisions 1970). pp.4. Building Research Station Digest 90 (second series).

[49] SHACKLOCK, B.W. and KEENE, P.W. Comparison of the compressive and flexural strengths of concrete with and without entrained air. Civil Engineering. Vol. 54, No. 631. January 1959. C&CA Reprint No. 66.

[50] WRIGHT, P.J.F. The flexural strength of plain concrete. London, HMSO, 1964. pp.52. Road Research Technical Paper No.67.

[51] DEWAR, J.D. The indirect tensile strength of concrete of high compressive strength. London, Cement and Concrete Association, March 1964. pp.12. Technical Report 42.377.

[52] CHAPMAN, C.P. The cylinder splitting test. Concrete. Vol. 2, No. 2. February 1968. pp.77-85.

[53] WILSON, J.G. Specification clauses covering the production of high quality finishes to in-situ concrete. London, Cement and Concrete Association, June 1970. pp.13. Publication 47.010.

[54] SHACKLOCK, B.W. Factors affecting the selection of materials and production techniques for concrete. Appearance and weathering of concrete: seminar for architects, 7 May 1970. London, Cement and Concrete Association, 1970.

[55] WILSON, J.G. Exposed concrete finishes. Vol. 1. London, CR Books, 1962; New York, John Wiley, 1962. pp.144.

[56] SHACKLOCK, B.W. Air-entrained concrete: properties, mix design and quality control. The Surveyor. 27 August 1960. C&CA Reprint No. 76.

[57] DEWAR, J.D. Some effects of prolonged agitation of concrete. London, Cement and Concrete Association, December 1962. pp.18. Technical Report 42.367.

[58] AMERICAN SOCIETY FOR TESTING AND MATERIALS. Standard method of test for time of setting of concrete mixtures by penetration resistance. ASTM Standards. Part 10. October 1968. pp.293-296. ASTM Designation C403-68.

[59] TEYCHENNÉ, D.C. Lightweight aggregate concrete. Building Research Station symposium, 23 November 1966. Paper No. 1. pp.32.

[60] COMITÉ EUROPÉEN DU BÉTON. Lightweight concrete. May 1972. Information Bulletin No. 85.

[61] McINTOSH, J.D. The use in mass concrete of aggregate of large maximum size. Civil Engineering and Public Works

[62] Review. Vol. 52, No. 615. September 1957. C&CA Reprint No. 45.

[62] KEENE, P.W. The effect of air-entrainment on the shrinkage of concrete stored in laboratory air. London, Cement and Concrete Association, January 1960. pp.12. Technical Report 42.331.

[63] BUILDING RESEARCH STATION. Shrinkage of natural aggregates in concrete. Garston, June 1963 (revised March 1968). pp.5. Building Research Station Digest 35 (second series).

[64] BONNELL, D.G.R. and HARPER, F.C. Thermal expansion of concrete. London, HMSO, 1951. pp.22. National Building Studies Technical Paper No. 7.

[65] BROWNE, R.D. Properties of concrete in reactor vessels. Conference on prestressed concrete pressure vessels, Westminster, 13-17 March 1967. London, The Institution of Civil Engineers, 1968. Group C, Paper 13. pp.131-151.

[66] NEWMAN, K. The design of concrete mixes with high alumina cement. Reinforced Concrete Review. Vol. 5. March 1960. pp.269-301.

[67] BATE, S.C.C. et al. Handbook on the Unified Code for structural concrete (CP 110 : 1972). London, Cement and Concrete Association, 1972. pp.153. Publication 14.005.

[68] SHARP, D.R. Lean concrete and soil-cement in road and airfield bases: a review of current practice in Great Britain. Roads and Road Construction. February and March 1960. C&CA Reprint No. 74.

[69] CEMENT AND CONCRETE ASSOCIATION. Lean concrete bases for roads. London, February 1962. pp.17. Publication 46.004.

[70] WILLIAMS, R.I.T. The effect of cement content on the strength and elastic properties of dry lean concrete. London, Cement and Concrete Association, November 1962. pp.28. Technical Report 42.323.

[71] McINTOSH, J.D. and KOLEK, J. Concrete mixes for blocks. Concrete Building and Concrete Products. Vol. 40, No. 2. February 1965. pp.83-97.

[72] McINTOSH, J.D. Concrete mix design. Second edition. London, Cement and Concrete Association, 1966. pp.123. Publication 11.002.

[73] SAUL, A.G.A. Principles underlying the steam curing of concrete at atmospheric pressure. Magazine of Concrete Research. Vol. 2, No. 6. March 1951. pp.127-140.

[74] PLOWMAN, J.M. Maturity and the strength of concrete. Magazine of Concrete Research. Vol. 8, No. 22. March 1956. pp.13-22.

[75] SADGROVE, B.M. The early development of strength in concrete. London, Construction Industry Research and Information Association, July 1970. pp.43. Technical Note 12.

[76] WEAVER, J. and SADGROVE, B.M. Striking times of formwork — tables of curing periods to achieve given strengths. London, Construction Industry Research and Information Association, October 1971. pp.76. Report 36.

[77] HUMMELSHEJ, G.E. New method for the manufacture of hot concrete. Copenhagen, Thomas Schmidt, 1967.

[78] PINK, V.A. Winter concreting. London, Cement and Concrete Association, 1967. pp.24. Publication 45.007.

[79] KEMPSTER, E. Measuring void content: new apparatus for aggregates, sands and fillers. Contract Journal. Vol. 228 (4683). 27 March 1969. pp.409-410. Reprinted as BRS Current Paper CP 19/69.

[80] CEMENT AND CONCRETE ASSOCIATION. The determination of the proportions of aggregates approximating to any required grading. Second edition. London, 1969. Advisory note 45.012.

[81] KELLY, R.T. and VAIL, J.W. Rapid analysis of fresh concrete. Concrete. Vol. 2, No. 4, pp.140-145; Vol. 2, No. 5, pp.206-210. February and May 1968.

[82] BACKLER, A.P. Rapid analysis of fresh concrete. Conrad. Vol. 2, No. 1, April 1970. pp.21-22.

CONCRETE CONSTITUENTS AND MIX PROPORTIONS

BRITISH STANDARDS

BS 12.	Portland cement (ordinary and rapid-hardening).
Part 1 : 1958.	Imperial units.
Part 2 : 1971.	Metric units.
BS 146 : 1958.	Portland-blastfurnace cement.
BS 340 : 1963.	Precast concrete kerbs, channels, edgings and quadrants.
BS 812 : 1967.	Methods for sampling and testing of mineral aggregates, sands and fillers.
BS 877 : 1967.	Foamed or expanded blastfurnace slag lightweight aggregate for concrete.
BS 882/1201 : 1965.	Aggregates from natural sources for concrete (including granolithic).
BS 915 : 1947.	High alumina cement.
BS 1014 : 1961.	Pigments for cement, magnesium oxychloride and concrete.
BS 1047 : 1952.	Air-cooled blastfurnace slag coarse aggregate for concrete.
BS 1165 : 1966.	Clinker aggregate for concrete.
BS 1370 : 1958.	Low heat Portland cement.
BS 1881.	Methods of testing concrete.
Part 1 : 1970.	Methods of sampling fresh concrete.
Part 2 : 1970.	Methods of testing fresh concrete.
Part 3 : 1970.	Methods of making and curing test specimens.
Part 4 1970.	Methods of testing concrete for strength.
Part 5 : 1970.	Methods of testing hardened concrete for other than strength.
Part 6 : 1971.	Analysis of hardened concrete.
BS 2028/1364 : 1968.	Precast concrete blocks.
BS 3148 : 1959.	Tests for water for making concrete.
BS 3797 : 1964.	Lightweight aggregates for concrete.
BS 3892 : 1965.	Pulverized-fuel ash for use in concrete.
BS 4027.	Sulphate-resisting Portland cement.
Part 1 : 1966.	Imperial units.
Part 2 : 1972.	Metric units.
BS 4246 : 1968.	Low heat Portland-blastfurnace cement.
BS 4248 : 1968.	Supersulphated cement.
BS 4550.	Methods of testing cement.
Part 2 : 1970.	Chemical tests.

CODES OF PRACTICE

CP 110 : 1972.	The structural use of concrete.
CP 111.	Structural recommendations for loadbearing walls.
Part 1 : 1964.	Imperial units.
Part 2 : 1970.	Metric units.
CP 114.	Structural use of reinforced concrete in buildings.
Part 1 : 1957.	Imperial units.
Part 2 : 1969.	Metric units
CP 115.	The structural use of prestressed concrete in buildings.
Part 1 : 1959.	Imperial units.
Part 2 : 1969.	Metric units.
CP 116.	The structural use of precast concrete.
Part 1 : 1965.	Imperial units.
Part 2 : 1969.	Metric units.
CP 2007.	Design and construction of reinforced and prestressed concrete structures for the storage of water and other aqueous liquids.
Part 1 : 1960.	Imperial units.
Part 2 : 1970.	Metric units.